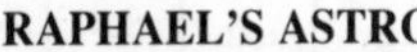

RAPHAEL'S ASTRO

Ephemeris of the P

for 1997

A Complete Aspectarian

Mean Obliquity of the Ecliptic, 1997, 23° 26′ 23″

INTRODUCTION

Greenwich Mean Time (G.M.T.) has been used as the basis for all tabulations and times. The tabular data are for Greenwich Mean Noon (12h. G.M.T.), except for the Moon tabulations headed "MIDNIGHT". All phenomena and aspect times are now in G.M.T.

This edition follows the layout for the new form which was introduced in 1980.

BRITISH SUMMER TIME

British Summer Time begins on March 30 and ends on October 26. When *British Summer Time* (one hour in advance of G.M.T.) is used, subtract one hour from B.S.T. before entering this Ephemeris.

These dates are correct according to the acts in force at the time of printing.

Printed in Great Britain

ISBN 0-572-02115-1

Published by

LONDON: W. FOULSHAM & CO. LTD.

BENNETS CLOSE, CIPPENHAM, BERKS. ENGLAND

NEW YORK TORONTO CAPE TOWN SYDNEY

NEW MOON-Jan. 9, 4h.26m. am. (18°♑57′)

D M	D W	Sidereal Time H. M. S.	☉ Long. ° ′ ″	☉ Dec. ° ′	☽ Long. ° ′ ″	☽ Lat. ° ′	☽ Dec. ° ′	☽ Node ° ′	Midnight ☽ Long. ° ′ ″	Midnight ☽ Dec. ° ′
1	W	18 44 42	11 ♑ 7 2	22 S 58	4 ♎ 44 47	0 N 12	1 S 42	3 ♎ 2	10 ♎ 48 39	3 S 36
2	Th	18 48 39	12 8 12	22 53	16 56 35	1 16	5 29	2 59	23 9 15	7 20
3	F	18 52 35	13 9 22	22 47	29 27 21	2 18	9 8	2 55	5 ♏ 51 27	10 50
4	S	18 56 32	14 10 32	22 41	12 ♏ 22 6	3 15	12 27	2 52	18 59 44	13 56
5	Su	19 0 29	15 11 42	22 34	25 44 39	4 3	15 15	2 49	2 ♐ 37 1	16 23
6	M	19 4 25	16 12 53	22 27	9 ♐ 36 46	4 39	17 17	2 46	16 43 41	17 57
7	T	19 8 22	17 14 4	22 20	23 57 18	4 59	18 20	2 43	1 ♑ 16 57	18 24
8	W	19 12 18	18 15 15	22 12	8 ♑ 41 46	4 59	18 10	2 39	16 10 39	17 37
9	Th	19 16 15	19 16 25	22 3	23 42 26	4 40	16 46	2 36	1 ♒ 15 50	15 36
10	F	19 20 11	20 17 35	21 54	8 ♒ 49 31	4 0	14 11	2 33	16 22 13	12 31
11	S	19 24 8	21 18 45	21 45	23 52 45	3 4	10 39	2 30	1 ♓ 20 4	8 38
12	Su	19 28 4	22 19 55	21 35	8 ♓ 43 19	1 57	6 30	2 27	16 1 48	4 S 17
13	M	19 32 1	23 21 3	21 25	23 15 2	0 N 42	2 S 2	2 24	0 ♈ 22 42	0 N 13
14	T	19 35 58	24 22 11	21 15	7 ♈ 24 42	0 S 33	2 N 26	2 20	14 21 1	4 35
15	W	19 39 54	25 23 19	21 4	21 11 47	1 44	6 39	2 17	27 57 13	8 36
16	Th	19 43 51	26 24 25	20 52	4 ♉ 37 36	2 48	10 25	2 14	11 ♉ 13 17	12 5
17	F	19 47 47	27 25 31	20 40	17 44 35	3 42	13 34	2 11	24 11 52	14 53
18	S	19 51 44	28 26 36	20 28	0 ♊ 35 27	4 22	16 0	2 8	6 ♊ 55 40	16 54
19	Su	19 55 40	29 ♑ 27 40	20 16	13 12 49	4 50	17 35	2 5	19 27 8	18 4
20	M	19 59 37	0 ♒ 28 43	20 3	25 38 53	5 3	18 19	2 1	1 ♋ 48 14	18 22
21	T	20 3 33	1 29 46	19 49	7 ♋ 55 23	5 1	18 11	1 58	14 0 29	17 48
22	W	20 7 30	2 30 48	19 36	20 3 40	4 47	17 13	1 55	26 5 5	16 26
23	Th	20 11 27	3 31 49	19 22	2 ♌ 4 51	4 19	15 29	1 52	8 ♌ 3 8	14 22
24	F	20 15 23	4 32 49	19 7	14 0 6	3 40	13 6	1 49	19 55 55	11 43
25	S	20 19 20	5 33 48	18 53	25 50 51	2 52	10 12	1 45	1 ♍ 45 7	8 36
26	Su	20 23 16	6 34 47	18 38	7 ♍ 39 2	1 56	6 54	1 42	13 32 56	5 8
27	M	20 27 13	7 35 45	18 22	19 27 14	0 S 55	3 N 19	1 39	25 22 20	1 N 28
28	T	20 31 9	8 36 42	18 6	1 ♎ 18 44	0 N 8	0 S 24	1 36	7 ♎ 16 57	2 S 16
29	W	20 35 6	9 37 38	17 50	13 17 32	1 12	4 8	1 33	19 21 5	5 58
30	Th	20 39 2	10 38 34	17 34	25 28 13	2 14	7 46	1 30	1 ♏ 39 32	9 29
31	F	20 42 59	11 ♒ 39 29	17 S 17	7 ♏ 55 41	3 N 11	11 S 8	1 ♎ 26	14 ♏ 17 16	12 S 40

D M	Mercury Lat. ° ′	Mercury Dec. ° ′	Mercury Dec. ° ′	Venus Lat. ° ′	Venus Dec. ° ′	Venus Dec. ° ′	Mars Lat. ° ′	Mars Dec. ° ′	Mars Dec. ° ′	Jupiter Lat. ° ′	Jupiter Dec. ° ′
1	2 N 28	20 S 24	20 S 16	0 N 46	22 S 14	22 S 22	2 N 39	2 N 40	2 N 34	0 S 20	21 S 24
3	2 55	20 11	20 6	0 41	22 30	22 37	2 42	2 27	2 21	0 20	21 19
5	3 11	20 4	20 2	0 36	22 43	22 48	2 44	2 15	2 9	0 20	21 14
7	3 18	20 3	20 4	0 30	22 53	22 57	2 47	2 3	1 57	0 20	21 9
9	3 16	20 7	20 12	0 25	23 1	23 4	2 49	1 52	1 47	0 21	21 4
11	3 7	20 17	20 24	0 20	23 6	23 7	2 52	1 42	1 37	0 21	20 58
13	2 53	20 31	20 39	0 15	23 8	23 7	2 55	1 32	1 28	0 21	20 53
15	2 37	20 47	20 56	0 10	23 7	23 5	2 57	1 23	1 19	0 21	20 48
17	2 18	21 4	21 13	0 N 4	23 3	23 0	3 0	1 15	1 12	0 21	20 42
19	1 58	21 21	21 29	0 S 1	22 56	22 52	3 3	1 8	1 5	0 21	20 36
21	1 38	21 37	21 44	0 6	22 47	22 41	3 6	1 2	1 0	0 22	20 30
23	1 18	21 50	21 56	0 11	22 35	22 28	3 8	0 57	0 55	0 22	20 25
25	0 58	22 0	22 4	0 16	22 20	22 12	3 11	0 53	0 51	0 22	20 19
27	0 39	22 8	22 10	0 21	22 2	21 53	3 14	0 50	0 48	0 22	20 13
29	0 20	22 11	22 S 11	0 26	21 42	21 S 31	3 17	0 47	0 N 47	0 22	20 7
31	0 N 3	22 S 10		0 S 30	21 S 19		3 N 19	0 N 46		0 S 23	20 S 1

FIRST QUARTER-Jan.15, 8h. 2m. pm. (25°♈44′)

FULL MOON-Jan.23, 3h.11m. pm. (3°♌40′)

EPHEMERIS]			JANUARY 1997														3
D	☿	♀	♂	♃	♄	♅	♆	♇	Lunar Aspects								
M	Long.	Long.	Long.	Long.	Long.	Long.	Long.	Long.	☉	☿	♀	♂	♃	♄	♅	♆	♇
	° ′	° ′	° ′	° ′	° ′	° ′	° ′	° ′									
1	12♑26	19♐ 4	29♍24	25♑17	1♈22	3♒18	26♑51	4♐24				☌		☍	△		⚹
2	11R 5	20 19	29♍44	25 31	1 25	3 21	26 53	4 26	□	□	⚹						∠
3	9 44	21 34	0♎ 3	25 45	1 28	3 25	26 55	4 28				⚺	□		□	□	⚺
4	8 27	22 50	0 22	25 59	1 31	3 28	26 57	4 30	⚹	⚹	∠	∠		⚼			
5	7 15	24 5	0 40	26 13	1 35	3 31	27 0	4 32	∠	∠	⚺	⚹	⚹	△		⚹	
6	6 10	25 20	0 58	26 27	1 38	3 35	27 2	4 34		⚺			∠		⚹	∠	☌
7	5 14	26 35	1 16	26 41	1 42	3 38	27 4	4 36	⚺		☌		⚺		∠	⚺	
8	4 27	27 50	1 33	26 55	1 45	3 41	27 6	4 38		☌		□		□	⚺		⚺
9	3 50	29♐ 5	1 50	27 9	1 49	3 45	27 9	4 40	☌		⚺		☌			☌	∠
10	3 23	0♑20	2 6	27 23	1 53	3 48	27 11	4 41		⚺	∠	△		⚹	☌		⚹
11	3 6	1 35	2 22	27 37	1 57	3 52	27 13	4 43	⚺	∠		⚼	⚺	∠		⚺	
12	2 59	2 51	2 37	27 51	2 1	3 55	27 16	4 45	∠	⚹	⚹		∠	⚺	⚺	∠	□
13	3D 0	4 6	2 52	28 5	2 5	3 59	27 18	4 47	⚹				⚹		∠	⚹	
14	3 9	5 21	3 6	28 19	2 9	4 2	27 20	4 48		□	□	☍		☌	⚹		△
15	3 26	6 36	3 20	28 33	2 14	4 6	27 22	4 50	□							□	⚼
16	3 50	7 51	3 33	28 48	2 18	4 9	27 25	4 52		△	△		□	⚺	□		
17	4 20	9 6	3 46	29 2	2 22	4 13	27 27	4 53		⚼		⚼		∠			
18	4 56	10 21	3 58	29 16	2 27	4 16	27 29	4 55	△		⚼	△	△	⚹	△	△	☍
19	5 37	11 36	4 10	29 30	2 32	4 20	27 31	4 57	⚼				⚼		⚼	⚼	
20	6 22	12 52	4 21	29 44	2 36	4 23	27 34	4 58									
21	7 12	14 7	4 32	29♑58	2 41	4 27	27 36	5 0		☍		□		□			
22	8 5	15 22	4 42	0♒12	2 46	4 30	27 38	5 1			☍						⚼
23	9 2	16 37	4 51	0 26	2 51	4 34	27 41	5 3	☍			⚹	☍	△	☍	☍	△
24	10 2	17 52	5 0	0 40	2 56	4 37	27 43	5 4						⚼			
25	11 5	19 7	5 8	0 55	3 1	4 41	27 45	5 6		⚼		∠					
26	12 10	20 22	5 16	1 9	3 6	4 44	27 47	5 7		△	⚼	⚺				⚼	□
27	13 18	21 38	5 23	1 23	3 12	4 48	27 50	5 8	⚼		△		⚼		⚼		
28	14 27	22 53	5 29	1 37	3 17	4 51	27 52	5 10				☌	△	☍	△	△	⚹
29	15 39	24 8	5 35	1 51	3 22	4 55	27 54	5 11	△	□							
30	16 52	25 23	5 40	2 5	3 28	4 58	27 56	5 12			□					□	∠
31	18♑ 7	26♑38	5♎44	2♒19	3♈33	5♒ 2	27♑59	5♐14	□			⚺	□		□		⚺

D	Saturn		Uranus		Neptune		Pluto		Mutual Aspects
M	Lat.	Dec.	Lat.	Dec.	Lat.	Dec.	Lat.	Dec.	
	° ′	° ′	° ′	° ′	° ′	° ′	° ′	° ′	1 ♀⊥♃. ☿P♆. 2 ☉☌☿. ☿⊥♇. ♀⊥♆. 4 ☉P♀.
1	2S21	1S37	0S34	19S58	0N26	20S22	12N24	8S50	7 ♀⚺♃. ♀⚺♆.
3	2 21	1 34	0 34	19 57	0 26	20 21	12 24	8 50	8 ☿⚺♇. ♀⊥♅.
5	2 20	1 31	0 34	19 55	0 26	20 20	12 24	8 50	9 ☉∠♇. ☿⚺♅. ♂☍♄. ♃☌♆.
7	2 20	1 28	0 34	19 53	0 26	20 20	12 25	8 50	10 ☉Q♄. 11 ♀□♄. ☿P♆.
9	2 20	1 25	0 34	19 52	0 25	20 19	12 25	8 51	12 ☿☌♀. ♀□♂. ☿Stat. 13 ♀⚺♅. 14 ♀⚺♇.
11	2 19	1 21	0 34	19 50	0 25	20 18	12 26	8 51	15 ☿P♃. 16 ☉P☿.
13	2 19	1 18	0 34	19 49	0 25	20 17	12 26	8 51	17 ☉☌♆. ☿⚺♅. ☉P♃.
15	2 18	1 14	0 34	19 47	0 25	20 16	12 26	8 51	18 ☿⚺♇. ♀⊥♇.
17	2 18	1 10	0 34	19 45	0 25	20 15	12 27	8 51	19 ☉☌♃. ☉P♆. 20 ♂△♅.
19	2 18	1 6	0 34	19 44	0 25	20 14	12 27	8 51	22 ☉⚹♄. ☉P♅. ♂P♄. 24 ☉☌♅.
21	2 17	1 2	0 34	19 42	0 25	20 13	12 28	8 51	25 ☉△♂. ☉⚹♇. ☿⊥♇. ♂⚹♇.
23	2 17	0 58	0 34	19 40	0 25	20 13	12 29	8 51	26 ♀∠♇. ♂P♄.
25	2 17	0 53	0 34	19 39	0 25	20 12	12 29	8 51	27 ♀Q♄. ☿P♀.
27	2 16	0 49	0 34	19 37	0 25	20 11	12 30	8 51	28 ♃P♆.
29	2 16	0 44	0 34	19 35	0 25	20 10	12 30	8 51	
31	2S16	0S40	0S34	19S34	0N25	20S 9	12N31	8S51	

LAST QUARTER-Jan. 2, 1h.45m. am. (11°♎42′) & Jan.31, 7h.40m. pm. (11°♏59′)

NEW MOON-Feb. 7, 3h. 6m. pm. (18°♒53′)

D M	D W	Sidereal Time	☉ Long.	☉ Dec.	☽ Long.	☽ Lat.	☽ Dec.	☽ Node	Midnight ☽ Long.	Midnight ☽ Dec.
		H. M. S.	° ′ ″	° ′	° ′ ″	° ′	° ′	° ′	° ′ ″	° ′
1	S	20 46 56	12 ♒ 40 23	17 S 0	20 ♏ 44 51	4 N 1	14 S 4	1 ♎ 23	27 ♏ 18 57	15 S 19
2	Su	20 50 52	13 41 17	16 43	4 ♐ 0 0	4 39	16 23	1 20	10 ♐ 48 18	17 14
3	M	20 54 49	14 42 10	16 25	17 44 2	5 3	17 51	1 17	24 47 11	18 12
4	T	20 58 45	15 43 2	16 7	1 ♑ 57 35	5 9	18 16	1 14	9 ♑ 14 50	18 3
5	W	21 2 42	16 43 53	15 49	16 38 17	4 56	17 30	1 11	24 7 7	16 40
6	Th	21 6 38	17 44 43	15 31	1 ♒ 40 17	4 22	15 31	1 7	9 ♒ 16 36	14 6
7	F	21 10 35	18 45 32	15 12	16 54 44	3 30	12 26	1 4	24 33 21	10 33
8	S	21 14 31	19 46 19	14 53	2 ♓ 11 4	2 22	8 29	1 1	9 ♓ 46 35	6 18
9	Su	21 18 28	20 47 5	14 34	17 18 43	1 N 4	4 S 1	0 58	24 46 28	1 S 42
10	M	21 22 25	21 47 50	14 14	2 ♈ 8 58	0 S 16	0 N 37	0 55	9 ♈ 25 35	2 N 53
11	T	21 26 21	22 48 33	13 55	16 35 54	1 34	5 5	0 51	23 39 39	7 11
12	W	21 30 18	23 49 14	13 35	0 ♉ 36 45	2 43	9 8	0 48	7 ♉ 27 17	10 57
13	Th	21 34 14	24 49 54	13 15	14 11 25	3 41	12 34	0 45	20 49 27	14 1
14	F	21 38 11	25 50 32	12 54	27 21 45	4 26	15 15	0 42	3 ♊ 48 43	16 17
15	S	21 42 7	26 51 9	12 34	10 ♊ 10 47	4 56	17 6	0 39	16 28 26	17 41
16	Su	21 46 4	27 51 44	12 13	22 42 5	5 11	18 4	0 36	28 52 13	18 13
17	M	21 50 0	28 52 16	11 52	4 ♋ 59 15	5 11	18 10	0 32	11 ♋ 3 35	17 54
18	T	21 53 57	29 ♒ 52 48	11 31	17 5 37	4 58	17 25	0 29	23 5 42	16 46
19	W	21 57 54	0 ♓ 53 17	11 9	29 4 10	4 31	15 55	0 26	5 ♌ 1 18	14 54
20	Th	22 1 50	1 53 45	10 48	10 ♌ 57 25	3 53	13 45	0 23	16 52 46	12 26
21	F	22 5 47	2 54 11	10 26	22 47 35	3 5	11 0	0 20	28 42 8	9 27
22	S	22 9 43	3 54 35	10 4	4 ♍ 36 38	2 9	7 49	0 16	10 ♍ 31 20	6 6
23	Su	22 13 40	4 54 58	9 42	16 26 29	1 7	4 19	0 13	22 22 21	2 N 29
24	M	22 17 36	5 55 19	9 20	28 19 12	0 S 2	0 N 38	0 10	4 ♎ 17 19	1 S 14
25	T	22 21 33	6 55 38	8 58	10 ♎ 17 4	1 N 3	3 S 6	0 7	16 18 46	4 57
26	W	22 25 29	7 55 56	8 36	22 22 47	2 7	6 45	0 4	28 29 33	8 29
27	Th	22 29 26	8 56 12	8 13	4 ♏ 39 28	3 6	10 9	0 1	10 ♏ 53 0	11 43
28	F	22 33 23	9 ♓ 56 27	7 S 50	17 ♏ 10 34	3 N 57	13 S 10	29 ♍ 57	23 ♏ 32 38	14 S 29

D M	Mercury Lat.	Mercury Dec.	Mercury Dec.	Venus Lat.	Venus Dec.	Venus Dec.	Mars Lat.	Mars Dec.	Mars Dec.	Jupiter Lat.	Jupiter Dec.
	° ′	° ′	° ′	° ′	° ′	° ′	° ′	° ′	° ′	° ′	° ′
1	0 S 6	22 S 8	22 S 5	0 S 33	21 S 7	20 S 54	3 N 21	0 N 46	0 N 46	0 S 23	19 S 57
3	0 22	22 0	21 55	0 37	20 40	20 26	3 23	0 47	0 47	0 23	19 51
5	0 38	21 48	21 40	0 41	20 11	19 55	3 26	0 48	0 49	0 23	19 45
7	0 52	21 31	21 20	0 46	19 39	19 23	3 28	0 51	0 52	0 23	19 39
9	1 6	21 8	20 55	0 50	19 5	18 48	3 31	0 54	0 57	0 24	19 32
11	1 18	20 41	20 25	0 54	18 29	18 10	3 33	0 59	1 2	0 24	19 26
13	1 29	20 8	19 50	0 57	17 51	17 31	3 36	1 5	1 9	0 24	19 19
15	1 39	19 31	19 10	1 1	17 11	16 50	3 38	1 13	1 16	0 24	19 13
17	1 47	18 48	18 24	1 4	16 29	16 7	3 40	1 21	1 25	0 24	19 6
19	1 55	17 59	17 33	1 7	15 45	15 22	3 42	1 30	1 35	0 25	19 0
21	2 0	17 6	16 37	1 10	14 59	14 35	3 43	1 40	1 46	0 25	18 53
23	2 5	16 7	15 35	1 13	14 11	13 47	3 45	1 52	1 58	0 25	18 47
25	2 7	15 2	14 28	1 15	13 22	12 57	3 46	2 4	2 11	0 25	18 40
27	2 9	13 53	13 16	1 17	12 32	12 6	3 47	2 17	2 24	0 26	18 33
29	2 8	12 38	11 S 58	1 19	11 40	11 S 14	3 48	2 32	2 N 39	0 26	18 27
31	2 S 6	11 S 18		1 S 21	10 S 47		3 N 48	2 N 46		0 S 26	18 S 20

FIRST QUARTER-Feb.14, 8h.58m. am. (25° ♉ 43′)

FULL MOON-Feb.22,10h.27m. am. (3°♍51′)

D M	☿ Long.	♀ Long.	♂ Long.	♃ Long.	♄ Long.	♅ Long.	♆ Long.	♇ Long.	☉	☿	♀	♂	♃	♄	♅	♆	♇
	° ′	° ′	° ′	° ′	° ′	° ′	° ′	° ′									
1	19♑24	27♑53	5♎48	2♒33	3♈39	5♒ 5	28♑ 1	5♐ 15		⚹		∠		⚼			
2	20 42	29♑ 8	5 51	2 47	3 44	5 9	28 3	5 16		∠	⚹	⚹	⚹	△	⚹	⚹	☌
3	22 1	0♒24	5 53	3 1	3 50	5 12	28 5	5 17	⚹	⚺	∠		∠		∠	∠	
4	23 22	1 39	5 55	3 15	3 56	5 16	28 7	5 18	∠		⚺	□	⚺	□	⚺	⚺	⚺
5	24 44	2 54	5 55	3 29	4 2	5 19	28 10	5 19	⚺								∠
6	26 7	4 9	5R 55	3 43	4 8	5 23	28 12	5 20		☌	☌	△	☌	⚹	☌	☌	⚹
7	27 31	5 24	5 55	3 57	4 14	5 26	28 14	5 21	☌			⚼		∠			
8	28♑56	6 39	5 53	4 11	4 20	5 30	28 16	5 22		⚺	⚺		⚺	⚺	⚺	⚺	□
9	0♒22	7 54	5 51	4 25	4 26	5 33	28 18	5 23	⚺	∠	∠		∠		∠	∠	
10	1 49	9 9	5 48	4 39	4 32	5 37	28 20	5 24	∠	⚹		☍	⚹	☌	⚹	⚹	△
11	3 17	10 25	5 44	4 52	4 38	5 40	28 23	5 25	⚹		⚹						⚼
12	4 46	11 40	5 39	5 6	4 45	5 43	28 25	5 26		□			□	⚺	□	□	
13	6 16	12 55	5 34	5 20	4 51	5 47	28 27	5 27			□	⚼		∠			
14	7 47	14 10	5 28	5 34	4 57	5 50	28 29	5 28	□							△	
15	9 18	15 25	5 21	5 47	5 4	5 54	28 31	5 28		△	△	△	△	⚹	△	⚼	☍
16	10 51	16 40	5 13	6 1	5 10	5 57	28 33	5 29	△	⚼			⚼		⚼		
17	12 25	17 55	5 5	6 15	5 17	6 0	28 35	5 30			⚼	□		□			
18	13 59	19 10	4 56	6 28	5 23	6 4	28 37	5 30	⚼								⚼
19	15 34	20 25	4 46	6 42	5 30	6 7	28 39	5 31				⚹				☍	
20	17 11	21 40	4 35	6 55	5 36	6 10	28 41	5 32					☍	△	☍		△
21	18 48	22 55	4 23	7 9	5 43	6 13	28 43	5 32		☍	☍	∠		⚼			
22	20 26	24 10	4 11	7 22	5 50	6 17	28 45	5 33	☍			⚺					□
23	22 5	25 25	3 58	7 35	5 57	6 20	28 47	5 33							⚼	⚼	
24	23 45	26 40	3 44	7 49	6 4	6 23	28 49	5 34				☌	⚼			△	
25	25 26	27 55	3 30	8 2	6 10	6 26	28 51	5 34		⚼	⚼		△	☍	△		⚹
26	27 8	29♒10	3 14	8 15	6 17	6 29	28 53	5 34	⚼	△							∠
27	28 51	0♓25	2 58	8 28	6 24	6 32	28 54	5 35	△		△	⚺	□		□	□	⚺
28	0♓35	1♓40	2♎42	8♒42	6♈31	6♒35	28♑56	5♐ 35				∠		⚼			

D M	Saturn Lat.	Saturn Dec.	Uranus Lat.	Uranus Dec.	Neptune Lat.	Neptune Dec.	Pluto Lat.	Pluto Dec.
	° ′	° ′	° ′	° ′	° ′	° ′	° ′	° ′
1	2S15	0S37	0S34	19S33	0N25	20S 9	12N31	8S50
3	2 15	0 33	0 34	19 31	0 25	20 8	12 32	8 50
5	2 15	0 28	0 34	19 29	0 25	20 7	12 32	8 50
7	2 15	0 23	0 34	19 28	0 25	20 6	12 33	8 50
9	2 14	0 18	0 34	19 26	0 25	20 5	12 34	8 49
11	2 14	0 12	0 34	19 24	0 25	20 4	12 34	8 49
13	2 14	0 7	0 34	19 23	0 25	20 4	12 35	8 49
15	2 13	0 2	0 34	19 21	0 25	20 3	12 36	8 48
17	2 13	0 3	0 34	19 20	0 25	20 2	12 37	8 48
19	2 13	0 9	0 34	19 18	0 25	20 1	12 37	8 47
21	2 13	0 14	0 34	19 16	0 25	20 0	12 38	8 47
23	2 13	0 20	0 35	19 15	0 25	20 0	12 39	8 46
25	2 12	0 25	0 35	19 13	0 25	19 59	12 39	8 46
27	2 12	0 31	0 35	19 12	0 25	19 58	12 40	8 45
29	2 12	0 37	0 35	19 10	0 25	19 57	12 41	8 44
31	2S12	0N42	0S35	19S 9	0N25	19S56	12N41	8S44

Mutual Aspects

1 ♀☌♆. 2 ☿∠♇.
3 ☿Q♄.
5 ♅⚹♇. ♀P♆.
6 ☉Q♇. ♀☌♃. ♀⚹♄. ♂Stat.
7 ♀△♂. ♀☌♅. ♀⚹♇. ♀P♃.
8 ☉∠♄. ☿☌♆ ♀P♅.
9 ☉⚼♂. ♃⚹♄.
12 ☿☌♃. ☿⚹♄. ☿⚹♇. ♂△♅. ♃P♅.
13 ☿△♂. ☿☌♅. ☿P♆.
14 ♂△♃. ♂⚹♇. ♃⚹♇.
15 ☿P♅.
16 ♂☍♄. ♃☌♅. ☿P♃.
17 ☉±♂. ☉⊥♄. ☉⚺♆. ♀Q♇.
19 ♀⚼♂. ♀∠♄. ♄△♇.
20 ☿Q♇. 21 ☿⚼♂.
22 ☉⚻♂. ☿∠♄.
23 ☉⊥♆.
24 ☉⚺♄. ☉⚺♅. ☉□♇.
25 ♀±♂.
26 ☉⚺♃. ☿±♂. ♀⚺♆. ☉P♇.
27 ☿⚺♆. ♀⊥♄.
28 ☿⊥♄.

NEW MOON-Mar. 9, 1h.15m. am. (18°♓31′)

D M	D W	Sidereal Time	☉ Long.	☉ Dec.	☽ Long.	☽ Lat.	☽ Dec.	☽ Node	Midnight ☽ Long.	Midnight ☽ Dec.
		H. M. S.	° ′ ″	° ′	° ′ ″	° ′	° ′	° ′	° ′ ″	° ′
1	S	22 37 19	10 ♓ 56 41	7 S 28	29 ♏ 59 39	4 N38	15 S 37	29 ♍ 54	6 ♐ 32 2	16 S 35
2	Su	22 41 16	11 56 53	7 5	13 ♐ 10 10	5 5	17 20	29 51	19 54 20	17 51
3	M	22 45 12	12 57 3	6 42	26 44 48	5 17	18 7	29 48	3 ♑ 41 41	18 8
4	T	22 49 9	13 57 12	6 19	10 ♑ 44 58	5 10	17 51	29 45	17 54 31	17 17
5	W	22 53 5	14 57 19	5 56	25 10 0	4 44	16 27	29 42	2 ♒ 30 57	15 19
6	Th	22 57 2	15 57 25	5 32	9 ♒ 56 41	3 59	13 55	29 38	17 26 23	12 17
7	F	23 0 58	16 57 29	5 9	24 59 3	2 56	10 25	29 35	2 ♓ 33 37	8 23
8	S	23 4 55	17 57 31	4 46	10 ♓ 8 52	1 41	6 12	29 32	17 43 37	3 S 55
9	Su	23 8 52	18 57 32	4 22	25 16 38	0 N19	1 S 35	29 29	2 ♈ 46 49	0 N46
10	M	23 12 48	19 57 30	3 59	10 ♈ 13 6	1 S 4	3 N 4	29 26	17 34 36	5 19
11	T	23 16 45	20 57 26	3 35	24 50 32	2 20	7 27	29 22	2 ♉ 0 22	9 26
12	W	23 20 41	21 57 21	3 11	9 ♉ 3 42	3 26	11 15	29 19	16 0 17	12 54
13	Th	23 24 38	22 57 13	2 48	22 50 5	4 18	14 19	29 16	29 33 9	15 32
14	F	23 28 34	23 57 3	2 24	6 ♊ 9 42	4 54	16 31	29 13	12 ♊ 40 2	17 16
15	S	23 32 31	24 56 51	2 0	19 4 34	5 13	17 47	29 10	25 23 43	18 4
16	Su	23 36 27	25 56 36	1 37	1 ♋ 37 59	5 18	18 8	29 7	7 ♋ 47 55	17 59
17	M	23 40 24	26 56 19	1 13	13 54 3	5 7	17 37	29 3	19 56 55	17 4
18	T	23 44 21	27 56 0	0 49	25 57 4	4 43	16 19	29 0	1 ♌ 55 2	15 24
19	W	23 48 17	28 55 39	0 26	7 ♌ 51 18	4 7	14 19	28 57	13 46 23	13 6
20	Th	23 52 14	29 ♓ 55 15	0 S 2	19 40 43	3 21	11 44	28 54	25 34 44	10 15
21	F	23 56 10	0 ♈ 54 50	0 N22	1 ♍ 28 51	2 26	8 40	28 51	7 ♍ 23 24	7 0
22	S	0 0 7	1 54 22	0 45	13 18 44	1 25	5 15	28 48	19 15 11	3 N27
23	Su	0 4 3	2 53 51	1 9	25 13 0	0 S 20	1 N36	28 44	1 ♎ 12 27	0 S 16
24	M	0 8 0	3 53 19	1 33	7 ♎ 13 48	0 N47	2 S 9	28 41	13 17 15	4 1
25	T	0 11 56	4 52 45	1 56	19 23 2	1 52	5 51	28 38	25 31 19	7 39
26	W	0 15 53	5 52 9	2 20	1 ♏ 42 21	2 53	9 21	28 35	7 ♏ 56 17	10 59
27	Th	0 19 50	6 51 31	2 43	14 13 20	3 47	12 30	28 32	20 33 41	13 52
28	F	0 23 46	7 50 51	3 7	26 57 33	4 30	15 6	28 28	3 ♐ 25 7	16 8
29	S	0 27 43	8 50 9	3 30	9 ♐ 56 35	5 0	16 59	28 25	16 32 8	17 37
30	Su	0 31 39	9 49 26	3 53	23 11 57	5 16	18 0	28 22	29 56 11	18 9
31	M	0 35 36	10 ♈ 48 41	4 N17	6 ♑ 44 57	5 N14	18 S 2	28 ♍ 19	13 ♑ 38 19	17 S 39

D M	Mercury Lat.	Mercury Dec.	Mercury Dec.	Venus Lat.	Venus Dec.	Venus Dec.	Mars Lat.	Mars Dec.	Mars Dec.	Jupiter Lat.	Jupiter Dec.
	° ′	° ′	° ′	° ′	° ′	° ′	° ′	° ′	° ′	° ′	° ′
1	2 S 8	12 S 38	11 S 58	1 S 19	11 S 40	11 S 14	3 N 48	2 N32	2 N 39	0 S 26	18 S 27
3	2 6	11 18	10 36	1 21	10 47	10 20	3 48	2 46	2 54	0 26	18 20
5	2 1	9 52	9 8	1 23	9 53	9 25	3 48	3 2	3 10	0 26	18 13
7	1 55	8 22	7 35	1 24	8 58	8 30	3 48	3 18	3 26	0 27	18 7
9	1 47	6 47	5 57	1 25	8 1	7 33	3 47	3 34	3 43	0 27	18 0
11	1 36	5 7	4 15	1 26	7 4	6 35	3 46	3 51	4 0	0 27	17 54
13	1 23	3 23	2 29	1 26	6 6	5 37	3 45	4 8	4 17	0 28	17 47
15	1 8	1 S 35	0 S 40	1 26	5 8	4 39	3 43	4 25	4 33	0 28	17 41
17	0 51	0 N16	1 N 12	1 26	4 9	3 39	3 41	4 42	4 50	0 28	17 34
19	0 32	2 8	3 5	1 26	3 9	2 40	3 39	4 58	5 6	0 28	17 28
21	0 S 11	4 2	4 58	1 25	2 10	1 40	3 36	5 14	5 22	0 29	17 21
23	0 N12	5 54	6 49	1 25	1 10	0 S 39	3 33	5 30	5 37	0 29	17 15
25	0 35	7 43	8 36	1 24	0 S 9	0 N21	3 30	5 45	5 52	0 29	17 9
27	1 0	9 28	10 18	1 22	0 N51	1 21	3 26	5 59	6 5	0 30	17 3
29	1 24	11 6	11 N 51	1 21	1 51	2 N22	3 22	6 12	6 N 18	0 30	16 57
31	1 N47	12 N35		1 S 19	2 N52		3 N 17	6 N24		0 S 30	16 S 50

FIRST QUARTER-Mar.16, 0h. 6m. am. (25°♊27′)

FULL MOON-Mar.24, 4h.45m. am. (3°♎35′)

D M	☿ Long.	♀ Long.	♂ Long.	♃ Long.	♄ Long.	♅ Long.	♆ Long.	♇ Long.
	° ′	° ′	° ′	° ′	° ′	° ′	° ′	° ′
1	2♓20	2♓55	2♎24	8♒55	6♈38	6♒38	28♑58	5♐35
2	4 6	4 10	2R 7	9 8	6 45	6 42	29 0	5 35
3	5 54	5 25	1 48	9 21	6 52	6 45	29 2	5 36
4	7 42	6 40	1 29	9 34	6 59	6 48	29 3	5 36
5	9 31	7 55	1 9	9 46	7 7	6 50	29 5	5 36
6	11 22	9 9	0 49	9 59	7 14	6 53	29 7	5 36
7	13 13	10 24	0 28	10 12	7 21	6 56	29 9	5 36
8	15 5	11 39	0♎ 7	10 25	7 28	6 59	29 10	5 36
9	16 59	12 54	29♍45	10 37	7 36	7 2	29 12	5R 36
10	18 54	14 9	29 23	10 50	7 43	7 5	29 13	5 36
11	20 49	15 24	29 1	11 2	7 50	7 8	29 15	5 36
12	22 46	16 39	28 38	11 15	7 57	7 10	29 17	5 36
13	24 43	17 53	28 15	11 27	8 5	7 13	29 18	5 36
14	26 41	19 8	27 52	11 39	8 12	7 16	29 20	5 35
15	28♓40	20 23	27 29	11 51	8 20	7 18	29 21	5 35
16	0♈39	21 38	27 6	12 4	8 27	7 21	29 23	5 35
17	2 38	22 52	26 42	12 16	8 34	7 24	29 24	5 35
18	4 38	24 7	26 19	12 28	8 42	7 26	29 25	5 34
19	6 38	25 22	25 55	12 39	8 49	7 29	29 27	5 34
20	8 37	26 36	25 32	12 51	8 57	7 31	29 28	5 34
21	10 36	27 51	25 8	13 3	9 4	7 34	29 30	5 33
22	12 33	29♓ 6	24 45	13 15	9 12	7 36	29 31	5 33
23	14 30	0♈20	24 22	13 26	9 19	7 38	29 32	5 32
24	16 25	1 35	23 59	13 38	9 27	7 41	29 33	5 32
25	18 17	2 50	23 37	13 49	9 34	7 43	29 35	5 31
26	20 8	4 4	23 14	14 0	9 42	7 45	29 36	5 31
27	21 55	5 19	22 52	14 11	9 49	7 47	29 37	5 30
28	23 39	6 33	22 31	14 23	9 57	7 50	29 38	5 29
29	25 19	7 48	22 10	14 34	10 4	7 52	29 39	5 29
30	26 55	9 2	21 49	14 44	10 12	7 54	29 40	5 28
31	28♈27	10♈17	21♍29	14♒55	10♈19	7♒56	29♑41	5♐27

Lunar Aspects

D M	☉	☿	♀	♂	♃	♄	♅	♆	♇
1		□	□	✱				✱	☌
2	□				✱	△	✱	∠	
3				□	∠		∠	⚺	
4	✱	✱	✱		⚺	□	⚺		⚺
5	∠	∠	∠	△				☌	∠
6	⚺	⚺	⚺	⚼	☌	✱	☌		✱
7						∠		⚺	
8		☌	☌		⚺	⚺	⚺	∠	□
9	☌			☍	∠		∠	✱	
10			⚺		✱	☌	✱		△
11	⚺	⚺	∠					□	⚼
12	∠	∠		⚼	□	⚺	□		
13	✱	✱	✱	△		∠		△	
14					△	✱	△		☍
15			□				⚼	⚼	
16	□	□		□	⚼				
17						□			
18	△		△	✱				☍	⚼
19		△	⚼	∠	☍	△	☍		△
20	⚼	⚼		⚺		⚼			
21									□
22								⚼	
23			☍	☌	⚼		⚼	△	
24	☍					☍	△		✱
25		☍		⚺	△				∠
26							□	□	⚺
27				∠	□				
28	⚼		⚼	✱		⚼		✱	
29	△	⚼	△		✱	△	✱	∠	☌
30		△		□	∠		∠	⚺	
31	□		□			□	⚺		⚺

D M	Saturn Lat.	Saturn Dec.	Uranus Lat.	Uranus Dec.	Neptune Lat.	Neptune Dec.	Pluto Lat.	Pluto Dec.
	° ′	° ′	° ′	° ′	° ′	° ′	° ′	° ′
1	2S12	0N37	0S35	19S10	0N25	19S57	12N41	8S44
3	2 12	0 42	0 35	19 9	0 25	19 56	12 41	8 44
5	2 12	0 48	0 35	19 7	0 25	19 56	12 42	8 43
7	2 12	0 54	0 35	19 6	0 25	19 55	12 43	8 43
9	2 12	1 0	0 35	19 4	0 25	19 54	12 44	8 42
11	2 12	1 6	0 35	19 3	0 25	19 54	12 44	8 41
13	2 11	1 11	0 35	19 2	0 25	19 53	12 45	8 40
15	2 11	1 17	0 35	19 0	0 25	19 52	12 46	8 40
17	2 11	1 23	0 35	18 59	0 25	19 52	12 46	8 39
19	2 11	1 29	0 35	18 58	0 25	19 51	12 47	8 38
21	2 11	1 35	0 35	18 57	0 25	19 51	12 48	8 37
23	2 11	1 41	0 35	18 56	0 25	19 50	12 48	8 37
25	2 11	1 47	0 35	18 54	0 25	19 50	12 49	8 36
27	2 11	1 53	0 35	18 53	0 25	19 49	12 49	8 35
29	2 11	1 59	0 35	18 52	0 25	19 49	12 50	8 34
31	2S11	2N 4	0S35	18S51	0N25	19S48	12N51	8S33

Mutual Aspects

1 ☿▽♂. ♀▽♂. ♄✱♅.
2 ☿☌♀.
3 ☉⊥♅. ☿⚺♅. ☿⊥♆. ☿□♇. ♀⊥♆.
♀□♇.
4 ☉∠♆. ☿⚺♄. ♀⚺♄. ♀⚺♅.
5 ☿⚺♃. ☿P♀.
6 ☉⊥♃.
7 ☿⊥♅. ♀⚺♃. ☿P♇.
8 ☿∠♆. ♀P♇. ♇Stat.
9 ☿⊥♃. ♀⊥♅.
10 ♀∠♆. ♂△♆. ☉P♂.
11 ☉☌☿.
12 ☉∠♅. ☿∠♅. ☿P♂.
13 ♀⊥♃.
14 ☿∠♃. ☉P☿.
15 ☿☍♂. ☿✱♆. ☿P♄.
16 ♂⚼♃. ♀P♂.
17 ☉☍♂. ☉∠♃. ♀∠♅. ☉P♄.
18 ☿△♇. ☉P☿. ☿P♄.
19 ☿✱♅. ♀☍♂.
20 ☉✱♆. ☿☌♄. ☿P♀.
21 ☿Q♆. ♀∠♃.
22 ☿✱♃. ♀✱♆. ♀P♄.
23 ☉P♀. ☿P♂.
25 ♂Q♇. ☉P♄.
26 ☉△♇. ☿Q♅. ☿⚼♇. ☿P♇.
27 ☿▽♂. ♀△♇. ♂⚼♅.
28 ☉✱♅.
29 ♀✱♅. ♀P♄.
30 ☉☌♄. ☿±♂. ☿Q♃.
31 ♀☌♄.

LAST QUARTER-Mar. 2, 9h.38m. am. (11°♐51′) & Mar.31, 7h.38m. pm. (11°♑ 8′)

NEW MOON-Apr. 7,11h. 2m. am. (17°♈40′)

D M	D W	Sidereal Time H. M. S.	☉ Long. ° ′ ″	☉ Dec. ° ′	☽ Long. ° ′ ″	☽ Lat. ° ′	☽ Dec. ° ′	☽ Node ° ′	Midnight ☽ Long. ° ′ ″	Midnight ☽ Dec. ° ′
1	T	0 39 32	11 ♈ 47 54	4 N40	20 ♑ 36 20	4 N54	17 S 0	28 ♍ 16	27 ♑ 38 54	16 S 6
2	W	0 43 29	12 47 5	5 3	4 ♒ 45 55	4 16	14 55	28 13	11 ♒ 57 7	13 30
3	Th	0 47 25	13 46 15	5 26	19 12 11	3 22	11 52	28 9	26 30 40	10 1
4	F	0 51 22	14 45 23	5 49	3 ♓ 51 59	2 13	8 1	28 6	11 ♓ 15 27	5 52
5	S	0 55 19	15 44 28	6 12	18 40 18	0 N55	3 S 38	28 3	26 5 41	1 S 20
6	Su	0 59 15	16 43 32	6 34	3 ♈ 30 40	0 S 26	0 N59	28 0	10 ♈ 54 19	3 N17
7	M	1 3 12	17 42 34	6 57	18 15 42	1 46	5 32	27 57	25 33 56	7 40
8	T	1 7 8	18 41 34	7 19	2 ♉ 48 9	2 57	9 40	27 54	9 ♉ 57 39	11 30
9	W	1 11 5	19 40 32	7 42	17 1 50	3 56	13 9	27 50	24 0 12	14 34
10	Th	1 15 1	20 39 28	8 4	0 ♊ 52 26	4 39	15 47	27 47	7 ♊ 38 22	16 44
11	F	1 18 58	21 38 22	8 26	14 17 57	5 5	17 27	27 44	20 51 18	17 56
12	S	1 22 54	22 37 13	8 48	27 18 37	5 15	18 10	27 41	3 ♋ 40 13	18 10
13	Su	1 26 51	23 36 2	9 10	9 ♋ 56 32	5 9	17 56	27 38	16 8 1	17 30
14	M	1 30 48	24 34 49	9 31	22 15 13	4 48	16 51	27 34	28 18 43	16 2
15	T	1 34 44	25 33 34	9 53	4 ♌ 19 7	4 16	15 2	27 31	10 ♌ 17 1	13 53
16	W	1 38 41	26 32 16	10 14	16 13 2	3 32	12 36	27 28	22 7 48	11 11
17	Th	1 42 37	27 30 56	10 35	28 1 54	2 40	9 39	27 25	3 ♍ 55 55	8 2
18	F	1 46 34	28 29 34	10 56	9 ♍ 50 24	1 41	6 19	27 22	15 45 53	4 33
19	S	1 50 30	29 ♈ 28 10	11 17	21 42 49	0 S 37	2 N43	27 19	27 41 40	0 N51
20	Su	1 54 27	0 ♉ 26 43	11 38	3 ♎ 42 48	0 N28	1 S 3	27 15	9 ♎ 46 34	2 S 56
21	M	1 58 23	1 25 15	11 58	15 53 16	1 34	4 49	27 12	22 3 7	6 39
22	T	2 2 20	2 23 44	12 18	28 16 19	2 35	8 26	27 9	4 ♏ 32 59	10 9
23	W	2 6 17	3 22 12	12 38	10 ♏ 53 13	3 31	11 45	27 6	17 17 1	13 14
24	Th	2 10 13	4 20 38	12 58	23 44 24	4 16	14 34	27 3	0 ♐ 15 19	15 43
25	F	2 14 10	5 19 2	13 18	6 ♐ 49 41	4 49	16 41	27 0	13 27 24	17 26
26	S	2 18 6	6 17 25	13 37	20 8 22	5 8	17 57	26 56	26 52 27	18 14
27	Su	2 22 3	7 15 46	13 56	3 ♑ 39 32	5 9	18 14	26 53	10 ♑ 29 29	17 59
28	M	2 25 59	8 14 5	14 15	17 22 13	4 53	17 28	26 50	24 17 35	16 41
29	T	2 29 56	9 12 23	14 34	1 ♒ 15 31	4 20	15 39	26 47	8 ♒ 15 52	14 23
30	W	2 33 52	10 ♉ 10 39	14 N52	15 ♒ 18 33	3 N31	12 S 53	26 ♍ 44	22 ♒ 23 23	11 S 12

D M	Mercury Lat. ° ′	Mercury Dec. ° ′	Mercury Dec. ° ′	Venus Lat. ° ′	Venus Dec. ° ′	Venus Dec. ° ′	Mars Lat. ° ′	Mars Dec. ° ′	Mars Dec. ° ′	Jupiter Lat. ° ′	Jupiter Dec. ° ′
1	1 N58	13 N16	13 N 55	1 S 18	3 N22	3 N52	3 N 15	6 N30	6 N 35	0 S 31	16 S 47
3	2 18	14 30	15 3	1 16	4 22	4 51	3 11	6 41	6 45	0 31	16 42
5	2 35	15 33	16 0	1 13	5 21	5 51	3 6	6 50	6 54	0 31	16 36
7	2 49	16 23	16 44	1 11	6 20	6 49	3 1	6 58	7 2	0 32	16 30
9	2 59	17 1	17 14	1 8	7 19	7 48	2 56	7 5	7 8	0 32	16 24
11	3 5	17 25	17 32	1 5	8 16	8 45	2 51	7 11	7 14	0 32	16 19
13	3 5	17 35	17 35	1 2	9 14	9 42	2 45	7 16	7 17	0 33	16 14
15	3 0	17 32	17 26	0 59	10 10	10 38	2 40	7 19	7 20	0 33	16 8
17	2 49	17 16	17 3	0 55	11 5	11 32	2 35	7 21	7 21	0 33	16 3
19	2 32	16 47	16 29	0 51	11 59	12 26	2 30	7 22	7 22	0 34	15 58
21	2 10	16 8	15 44	0 47	12 52	13 18	2 24	7 21	7 21	0 34	15 53
23	1 43	15 19	14 52	0 43	13 44	14 10	2 19	7 20	7 18	0 35	15 49
25	1 12	14 24	13 55	0 39	14 35	14 59	2 14	7 17	7 15	0 35	15 44
27	0 39	13 25	12 56	0 35	15 24	15 48	2 9	7 13	7 10	0 35	15 40
29	0 5	12 27	11 N 58	0 30	16 11	16 N35	2 4	7 8	7 N 5	0 36	15 35
31	0 S 29	11 N31		0 S 26	16 N57		1 N 59	7 N 1		0 S 36	15 S 31

FIRST QUARTER-Apr.14, 5h. 0m. pm. (24°♋47′)

FULL MOON-Apr.22, 8h.33m. pm. (2°♏45′)

D M	☿ Long.	♀ Long.	♂ Long.	♃ Long.	♄ Long.	♅ Long.	♆ Long.	♇ Long.
	° ′	° ′	° ′	° ′	° ′	° ′	° ′	° ′
1	29♈54	11♈31	21♍ 9	15♒ 6	10♈27	7♒58	29♑42	5♐ 27
2	1♉15	12 46	20R 50	15 17	10 34	8 0	29 43	5R 26
3	2 32	14 0	20 31	15 27	10 42	8 2	29 44	5 25
4	3 42	15 15	20 13	15 38	10 49	8 4	29 45	5 24
5	4 47	16 29	19 56	15 48	10 57	8 6	29 46	5 23
6	5 45	17 44	19 39	15 58	11 4	8 7	29 47	5 22
7	6 37	18 58	19 24	16 8	11 12	8 9	29 48	5 21
8	7 23	20 13	19 8	16 18	11 19	8 11	29 48	5 20
9	8 2	21 27	18 54	16 28	11 27	8 12	29 49	5 19
10	8 34	22 41	18 40	16 38	11 34	8 14	29 50	5 18
11	9 0	23 56	18 27	16 47	11 42	8 16	29 51	5 17
12	9 19	25 10	18 15	16 57	11 49	8 17	29 51	5 16
13	9 32	26 24	18 3	17 6	11 57	8 19	29 52	5 15
14	9 39	27 39	17 52	17 16	12 4	8 20	29 52	5 14
15	9R 39	28♈53	17 42	17 25	12 11	8 21	29 53	5 13
16	9 32	0♉ 7	17 33	17 34	12 19	8 23	29 54	5 12
17	9 21	1 21	17 25	17 43	12 26	8 24	29 54	5 11
18	9 3	2 36	17 17	17 52	12 34	8 25	29 54	5 9
19	8 41	3 50	17 11	18 0	12 41	8 26	29 55	5 8
20	8 14	5 4	17 5	18 9	12 48	8 28	29 55	5 7
21	7 43	6 18	16 59	18 17	12 55	8 29	29 56	5 6
22	7 9	7 32	16 55	18 25	13 3	8 30	29 56	5 4
23	6 32	8 46	16 51	18 34	13 10	8 31	29 56	5 3
24	5 53	10 0	16 48	18 42	13 17	8 32	29 57	5 2
25	5 13	11 14	16 46	18 49	13 24	8 33	29 57	5 0
26	4 32	12 28	16 45	18 57	13 32	8 33	29 57	4 59
27	3 52	13 42	16 44	19 5	13 39	8 34	29 57	4 57
28	3 13	14 56	16D 44	19 12	13 46	8 35	29 57	4 56
29	2 35	16 11	16 45	19 19	13 53	8 36	29 57	4 55
30	2♉ 0	17♉24	16♍47	19♒27	14♈ 0	8♒36	29♑57	4♐ 53

D M	Lunar Aspects ☉	☿	♀	♂	♃	♄	♅	♆	♇
1				△	⚺				∠
2		□		⚼		✶	☌	☌	✶
3	✶		✶		☌	∠			
4	∠	✶	∠			⚺	⚺	⚺	□
5	⚺	∠	⚺	☍	⚺		∠	∠	
6		⚺			∠		✶	✶	△
7	☌		●		✶	●			⚼
8		☌		⚼			□	□	
9	⚺		⚺	△	□	⚺			
10	∠					∠		△	☍
11		⚺	∠	□	△	✶	△	⚼	
12	✶	∠	✶		⚼		⚼		
13		✶				□			
14	□		□	✶					⚼
15		□		∠			☍	☍	△
16				⚺	☍	△			
17	△		△			⚼			
18	⚼	△						⚼	□
19		⚼	⚼	☌			⚼		
20					⚼		△	△	✶
21				⚺	△	☍			∠
22	☍			∠				□	
23		☍	☍	✶			□		⚺
24					□	⚼		✶	
25							✶		☌
26	⚼	⚼		□	✶	△	∠	∠	
27	△	△	⚼		∠		⚺	⚺	⚺
28			△	△	⚺	□			∠
29		□		⚼				☌	✶
30	□		□		☌	✶	☌		

D M	Saturn Lat.	Saturn Dec.	Uranus Lat.	Uranus Dec.	Neptune Lat.	Neptune Dec.	Pluto Lat.	Pluto Dec.
	° ′	° ′	° ′	° ′	° ′	° ′	° ′	° ′
1	2S11	2N 7	0S35	18S51	0N25	19S48	12N51	8S33
3	2 11	2 13	0 36	18 50	0 25	19 48	12 51	8 32
5	2 11	2 19	0 36	18 49	0 25	19 47	12 52	8 31
7	2 11	2 25	0 36	18 48	0 25	19 47	12 52	8 31
9	2 12	2 31	0 36	18 47	0 25	19 47	12 53	8 30
11	2 12	2 36	0 36	18 46	0 25	19 46	12 53	8 29
13	2 12	2 42	0 36	18 46	0 25	19 46	12 54	8 28
15	2 12	2 48	0 36	18 45	0 25	19 46	12 54	8 27
17	2 12	2 53	0 36	18 44	0 25	19 46	12 55	8 27
19	2 12	2 59	0 36	18 44	0 25	19 45	12 55	8 26
21	2 12	3 4	0 36	18 43	0 25	19 45	12 55	8 25
23	2 12	3 10	0 36	18 43	0 25	19 45	12 56	8 24
25	2 13	3 15	0 36	18 43	0 25	19 45	12 56	8 24
27	2 13	3 21	0 36	18 42	0 25	19 45	12 56	8 23
29	2 13	3 26	0 36	18 42	0 25	19 45	12 57	8 22
31	2S13	3N31	0S37	18S42	0N25	19S45	12N57	8S21

Mutual Aspects

1 ☉QΨ. ☿□Ψ. ☿±♇. ♀QΨ. ♂±♃.
2 ☉☌♀.
4 ♀✶♃.
5 ☉✶♃. ☿⚼♂.
6 ☿∇♇.
7 ♀∇♂. ☉P♂. ☿P♃.
8 ☉∇♂. ♀Q♅. ♀⚼♇. ♀P♂.
9 ☿□♅.
10 ☉Q♅. ☉⚼♇.
11 ♀±♂. ☉P♇. ♀P♇.
12 ♄QΨ. ☉P♀.
13 ☉±♂.
14 ♃Q♇.
15 ♀Q♃. ♀±♇. ☿Stat.
16 ♀□Ψ. ♂∇♃.
18 ♀⚼♂.
19 ☉□Ψ. ☉±♇.
20 ☉Q♃. ☿□♅. ♀∇♇.
22 ☉⚼♂. ☿☌♀. ☿P♃.
23 ♀□♅.
25 ☉☌☿. ☉∇♇. ☿∇♇. ☿P♀.
26 ☉P☿.
27 ♀⚺♄. ♂Stat.
28 ☉□♅. ♀P♃.
29 ♀△♂.
30 ☿⚼♂.

LAST QUARTER-Apr.30, 2h.37m. am. (9°♒48′)

NEW MOON-May 6, 8h.47m. pm. (16° ♉ 21′)

D M	D W	Sidereal Time	☉ Long.	☉ Dec.	☽ Long.	☽ Lat.	☽ Dec.	☽ Node	Midnight ☽ Long.	Midnight ☽ Dec.
		H. M. S.	° ′ ″	° ′	° ′ ″	° ′	° ′	° ′	° ′ ″	° ′
1	Th	2 37 49	11 ♉ 8 54	15 N10	29 ♒ 30 14	2 N28	9 S 20	26 ♍ 40	6 ♓ 38 52	7 S 19
2	F	2 41 46	12 7 7	15 28	13 ♓ 49 0	1 N16	5 12	26 37	21 0 21	2 S 59
3	S	2 45 42	13 5 19	15 46	28 12 29	0 S 1	0 S 44	26 34	5 ♈ 24 56	1 N32
4	Su	2 49 39	14 3 29	16 3	12 ♈ 37 13	1 18	3 N47	26 31	19 48 42	5 58
5	M	2 53 35	15 1 38	16 21	26 58 47	2 30	8 3	26 28	4 ♉ 6 47	10 1
6	T	2 57 32	15 59 45	16 37	11 ♉ 12 5	3 32	11 50	26 25	18 14 1	13 27
7	W	3 1 28	16 57 51	16 54	25 12 1	4 20	14 52	26 21	2 ♊ 5 34	16 3
8	Th	3 5 25	17 55 55	17 10	8 ♊ 54 13	4 51	16 59	26 18	15 37 41	17 41
9	F	3 9 21	18 53 57	17 26	22 15 44	5 6	18 7	26 15	28 48 18	18 19
10	S	3 13 18	19 51 58	17 42	5 ♋ 15 24	5 4	18 16	26 12	11 ♋ 37 13	17 59
11	Su	3 17 15	20 49 57	17 58	17 53 58	4 47	17 29	26 9	24 6 1	16 47
12	M	3 21 11	21 47 54	18 13	0 ♌ 13 49	4 18	15 54	26 5	6 ♌ 17 51	14 51
13	T	3 25 8	22 45 49	18 28	12 18 41	3 37	13 38	26 2	18 16 55	12 17
14	W	3 29 4	23 43 42	18 42	24 13 11	2 47	10 49	25 59	0 ♍ 8 9	9 15
15	Th	3 33 1	24 41 33	18 56	6 ♍ 2 29	1 51	7 35	25 56	11 56 51	5 50
16	F	3 36 57	25 39 23	19 10	17 51 54	0 S 49	4 2	25 53	23 48 17	2 N11
17	S	3 40 54	26 37 11	19 24	29 46 36	0 N14	0 N19	25 50	5 ♎ 47 26	1 S 35
18	Su	3 44 50	27 34 58	19 37	11 ♎ 51 18	1 18	3 S 29	25 46	17 58 40	5 22
19	M	3 48 47	28 32 43	19 50	24 9 56	2 20	7 12	25 43	0 ♏ 25 26	8 59
20	T	3 52 44	29 ♉ 30 26	20 3	6 ♏ 45 25	3 15	10 41	25 40	13 10 2	12 17
21	W	3 56 40	0 ♊ 28 8	20 15	19 39 19	4 2	13 45	25 37	26 13 16	15 4
22	Th	4 0 37	1 25 48	20 27	2 ♐ 51 44	4 38	16 11	25 34	9 ♐ 34 29	17 6
23	F	4 4 33	2 23 28	20 38	16 21 13	4 58	17 47	25 31	23 11 35	18 14
24	S	4 8 30	3 21 6	20 49	0 ♑ 5 10	5 2	18 24	25 27	7 ♑ 1 30	18 18
25	Su	4 12 26	4 18 43	21 0	14 0 8	4 49	17 55	25 24	21 0 37	17 16
26	M	4 16 23	5 16 19	21 11	28 2 31	4 17	16 21	25 21	5 ♒ 5 27	15 11
27	T	4 20 19	6 13 54	21 21	12 ♒ 9 6	3 30	13 47	25 18	19 13 8	12 11
28	W	4 24 16	7 11 28	21 31	26 17 21	2 30	10 24	25 15	3 ♓ 21 32	8 28
29	Th	4 28 13	8 9 1	21 40	10 ♓ 25 33	1 21	6 24	25 11	17 29 15	4 S 16
30	F	4 32 9	9 6 33	21 49	24 32 33	0 N 7	2 S 4	25 8	1 ♈ 35 17	0 N10
31	S	4 36 6	10 ♊ 4 5	21 N57	8 ♈ 37 20	1 S 7	2 N23	25 ♍ 5	15 ♈ 38 31	4 N34

D M	Mercury Lat.	Mercury Dec.	Mercury Dec.	Venus Lat.	Venus Dec.	Venus Dec.	Mars Lat.	Mars Dec.	Mars Dec.	Jupiter Lat.	Jupiter Dec.
	° ′	° ′	° ′	° ′	° ′	° ′	° ′	° ′	° ′	° ′	° ′
1	0 S 29	11 N31	11 N 5	0 S 26	16 N57	17 N20	1 N 59	7 N 1	6 N 58	0 S 36	15 S 31
3	1 2	10 41	10 19	0 21	17 41	18 3	1 54	6 54	6 50	0 37	15 28
5	1 32	9 59	9 42	0 17	18 24	18 44	1 49	6 46	6 42	0 37	15 24
7	2 0	9 27	9 14	0 12	19 4	19 24	1 44	6 37	6 32	0 37	15 20
9	2 23	9 4	8 56	0 7	19 43	20 1	1 39	6 27	6 21	0 38	15 17
11	2 43	8 51	8 48	0 S 2	20 19	20 36	1 35	6 16	6 10	0 38	15 14
13	2 59	8 48	8 50	0 N 3	20 53	21 9	1 30	6 4	5 57	0 39	15 11
15	3 12	8 54	9 0	0 8	21 25	21 40	1 26	5 51	5 44	0 39	15 8
17	3 20	9 9	9 20	0 13	21 54	22 8	1 22	5 37	5 30	0 40	15 6
19	3 26	9 32	9 47	0 17	22 21	22 33	1 18	5 23	5 15	0 40	15 4
21	3 28	10 3	10 21	0 22	22 45	22 57	1 13	5 8	5 0	0 41	15 2
23	3 27	10 41	11 2	0 27	23 7	23 17	1 10	4 52	4 44	0 41	15 0
25	3 23	11 24	11 48	0 32	23 26	23 35	1 6	4 36	4 27	0 42	14 58
27	3 16	12 13	12 39	0 37	23 43	23 50	1 2	4 18	4 10	0 42	14 57
29	3 7	13 6	13 N 34	0 41	23 56	24 N 2	0 58	4 1	3 N 51	0 43	14 56
31	2 S 55	14 N 3		0 N 46	24 N 7		0 N 54	3 N42		0 S 43	14 S 55

FIRST QUARTER-May 14,10h.55m. am. (23° ♌ 41′)

FULL MOON-May 22, 9h.13m. am. (1°♐19′)

D M	☿ Long.	♀ Long.	♂ Long.	♃ Long.	♄ Long.	♅ Long.	♆ Long.	♇ Long.	☉	☿	♀	♂	♃	♄	♅	♆	♇
	° ′	° ′	° ′	° ′	° ′	° ′	° ′	° ′									
1	1♉27	18♉38	16♍49	19♒34	14♈ 7	8♒37	29♑57	4♐52		⚹				∠		⚺	□
2	0R 58	19 52	16 52	19 40	14 14	8 38	29R 57	4R 50	⚹	∠	⚹	☍	⚺	⚺	⚺	∠	
3	0 32	21 6	16 56	19 47	14 21	8 38	29 57	4 49	∠	⚺			∠		∠	⚹	△
4	0♉10	22 20	17 1	19 54	14 28	8 39	29 57	4 47	⚺		∠			●	⚹		⚼
5	29♈53	23 34	17 6	20 0	14 35	8 39	29 57	4 46		●	⚺	⚼	⚹			□	
6	29 40	24 48	17 12	20 6	14 41	8 39	29 57	4 44	☌			△		⚺	□		
7	29 32	26 2	17 18	20 12	14 48	8 40	29 57	4 43		⚺	☌		□	∠		△	
8	29 29	27 16	17 25	20 18	14 55	8 40	29 57	4 41		∠				⚹	△	⚼	☍
9	29D 30	28 30	17 33	20 24	15 2	8 40	29 57	4 40	⚺			□	△		⚼		
10	29 36	29♉44	17 42	20 30	15 8	8 40	29 56	4 38	∠	⚹	⚺		⚼				
11	29♈46	0♊57	17 51	20 35	15 15	8 40	29 56	4 36	⚹		∠	⚹		□			⚼
12	0♉ 1	2 11	18 0	20 40	15 22	8 40	29 56	4 35		□	⚹	∠				☍	△
13	0 21	3 25	18 11	20 46	15 28	8R 40	29 55	4 33				⚺		△	☍		
14	0 44	4 39	18 21	20 51	15 35	8 40	29 55	4 32	□				☍				
15	1 13	5 52	18 33	20 55	15 41	8 40	29 55	4 30		△	□			⚼			□
16	1 45	7 6	18 45	21 0	15 47	8 40	29 54	4 28		⚼		☌			⚼	⚼	
17	2 21	8 20	18 58	21 4	15 54	8 40	29 54	4 27	△							△	⚹
18	3 1	9 34	19 11	21 9	16 0	8 40	29 53	4 25	⚼		△		⚼	☍	△		
19	3 45	10 47	19 24	21 13	16 6	8 39	29 53	4 24			⚼	⚺	△			□	∠
20	4 32	12 1	19 39	21 17	16 12	8 39	29 52	4 22		☍		∠			□		⚺
21	5 23	13 14	19 53	21 20	16 19	8 39	29 51	4 20				⚹	□				
22	6 18	14 28	20 9	21 24	16 25	8 38	29 51	4 19	☍					⚼	⚹	⚹	☌
23	7 15	15 42	20 24	21 27	16 31	8 38	29 50	4 17		⚼	☍	□	⚹	△		∠	
24	8 16	16 55	20 40	21 30	16 37	8 37	29 49	4 15					∠		∠	⚺	⚺
25	9 20	18 9	20 57	21 33	16 43	8 37	29 49	4 14	⚼	△				□	⚺		∠
26	10 27	19 22	21 14	21 36	16 48	8 36	29 48	4 12			⚼	△	⚺			☌	⚹
27	11 37	20 36	21 32	21 39	16 54	8 35	29 47	4 10	△	□		⚼		⚹	☌		
28	12 50	21 49	21 50	21 41	17 0	8 35	29 46	4 9			△		☌	∠		⚺	
29	14 5	23 3	22 8	21 44	17 6	8 34	29 46	4 7	□	⚹				⚺	⚺	∠	□
30	15 24	24 16	22 27	21 46	17 11	8 33	29 45	4 5		∠	□	☍	⚺		∠	⚹	
31	16♉45	25♊30	22♍46	21♒48	17♈17	8♒32	29♑44	4♐ 4	⚹				∠		⚹		△

D M	Saturn Lat.	Saturn Dec.	Uranus Lat.	Uranus Dec.	Neptune Lat.	Neptune Dec.	Pluto Lat.	Pluto Dec.
	° ′	° ′	° ′	° ′	° ′	° ′	° ′	° ′
1	2S13	3N31	0S37	18S42	0N25	19S45	12N57	8S21
3	2 13	3 36	0 37	18 41	0 25	19 45	12 57	8 21
5	2 14	3 41	0 37	18 41	0 25	19 45	12 57	8 20
7	2 14	3 46	0 37	18 41	0 25	19 45	12 57	8 19
9	2 14	3 51	0 37	18 41	0 25	19 45	12 57	8 19
11	2 14	3 56	0 37	18 41	0 25	19 45	12 58	8 18
13	2 15	4 1	0 37	18 41	0 25	19 45	12 58	8 18
15	2 15	4 6	0 37	18 41	0 25	19 45	12 58	8 17
17	2 15	4 10	0 37	18 41	0 25	19 46	12 58	8 17
19	2 16	4 15	0 37	18 42	0 25	19 46	12 58	8 16
21	2 16	4 19	0 37	18 42	0 25	19 46	12 57	8 16
23	2 16	4 23	0 37	18 42	0 25	19 46	12 57	8 15
25	2 17	4 28	0 37	18 42	0 25	19 47	12 57	8 15
27	2 17	4 32	0 37	18 43	0 25	19 47	12 57	8 14
29	2 17	4 36	0 38	18 43	0 25	19 47	12 57	8 14
31	2S18	4N40	0S38	18S44	0N25	19S48	12N57	8S14

Mutual Aspects

1 ☿ Q ♃. ♆ Stat.
2 ♀ □ ♃. ♀ ⊥ ♄. ☉ P ♃.
4 ☉ ⚺ ♄. 5 ☿ □ ♆.
6 ♀ P ♅.
7 ☉ △ ♂.
8 ☿ Stat.
9 ♀ P ♆.
10 ☿ ⚺ ♀. ♀ ∠ ♄. ♀ △ ♆.
11 ☉ □ ♃. ☉ ⊥ ♄.
12 ☿ □ ♆. 13 ♅ Stat.
14 ♀ ☍ ♇. ☉ P ♅.
17 ☿ ⊥ ♀. ♀ △ ♅.
18 ☿ Q ♃. 19 ☉ P ♆.
20 ☉ △ ♆. ☿ ⚼ ♂. ☿ ∇ ♇.
22 ☉ ∠ ♄. ♀ ⚼ ♆.
24 ☿ □ ♅. ♀ ⚹ ♄.
25 ☉ ☍ ♇. 26 ♂ P ♄.
27 ♂ ∇ ♃.
28 ♀ □ ♂. ♀ △ ♃.
29 ☉ △ ♅. ♀ ⚼ ♅. ♂ Q ♇.
30 ♀ ± ♆. 31 ☿ ⚺ ♄.

LAST QUARTER-May 29, 7h.51m. am. (7°♓59′)

NEW MOON-June 5, 7h. 4m. am. (14° ♊ 40′)

D M	D W	Sidereal Time	☉ Long.	☉ Dec.	☽ Long.	☽ Lat.	☽ Dec.	☽ Node	Midnight ☽ Long.	Midnight ☽ Dec.
		H. M. S.	° ′ ″	° ′	° ′ ″	° ′	° ′	° ′	° ′ ″	° ′
1	Su	4 40 2	11 ♊ 1 36	22 N 6	22 ♈ 38 39	2 S 17	6 N41	25 ♍ 2	29 ♈ 37 27	8 N42
2	M	4 43 59	11 59 6	22 13	6 ♉ 34 38	3 18	10 36	24 59	13 ♉ 29 53	12 19
3	T	4 47 55	12 56 35	22 21	20 22 49	4 7	13 53	24 56	27 13 3	15 13
4	W	4 51 52	13 54 4	22 28	4 ♊ 0 13	4 40	16 21	24 52	10 ♊ 43 56	17 15
5	Th	4 55 48	14 51 31	22 35	17 23 53	4 58	17 53	24 49	23 59 47	18 17
6	F	4 59 45	15 48 58	22 41	0 ♋ 31 25	5 0	18 27	24 46	6 ♋ 58 40	18 21
7	S	5 3 42	16 46 24	22 47	13 21 27	4 46	18 2	24 43	19 39 50	17 29
8	Su	5 7 38	17 43 48	22 52	25 53 56	4 18	16 44	24 40	2 ♌ 4 0	15 48
9	M	5 11 35	18 41 12	22 57	8 ♌ 10 19	3 39	14 42	24 37	14 13 16	13 26
10	T	5 15 31	19 38 35	23 2	20 13 20	2 51	12 3	24 33	26 11 0	10 32
11	W	5 19 28	20 35 56	23 6	2 ♍ 6 53	1 55	8 55	24 30	8 ♍ 1 33	7 14
12	Th	5 23 24	21 33 17	23 10	13 55 41	0 S 55	5 28	24 27	19 49 56	3 N39
13	F	5 27 21	22 30 37	23 14	25 45 0	0 N 7	1 N48	24 24	1 ♎ 41 34	0 S 5
14	S	5 31 17	23 27 55	23 17	7 ♎ 40 19	1 10	1 S 59	24 21	13 41 55	3 52
15	Su	5 35 14	24 25 13	23 19	19 46 59	2 10	5 44	24 17	25 56 8	7 33
16	M	5 39 11	25 22 30	23 21	2 ♏ 9 52	3 6	9 19	24 14	8 ♏ 28 40	11 0
17	T	5 43 7	26 19 46	23 23	14 52 52	3 54	12 34	24 11	21 22 46	14 1
18	W	5 47 4	27 17 2	23 25	27 58 28	4 31	15 18	24 8	4 ♐ 40 0	16 25
19	Th	5 51 0	28 14 17	23 26	11 ♐ 27 14	4 54	17 18	24 5	18 19 55	17 57
20	F	5 54 57	29 ♊ 11 31	23 26	25 17 37	5 1	18 21	24 2	2 ♑ 19 49	18 28
21	S	5 58 53	0 ♋ 8 45	23 26	9 ♑ 25 53	4 50	18 17	23 58	16 35 7	17 49
22	Su	6 2 50	1 5 58	23 26	23 46 44	4 20	17 4	23 55	0 ♒ 59 59	16 3
23	M	6 6 46	2 3 11	23 25	8 ♒ 14 5	3 34	14 46	23 52	15 28 19	13 15
24	T	6 10 43	3 0 24	23 24	22 42 4	2 34	11 32	23 49	29 54 43	9 38
25	W	6 14 40	3 57 37	23 23	7 ♓ 5 51	1 24	7 37	23 46	14 ♓ 15 6	5 29
26	Th	6 18 36	4 54 50	23 21	21 22 9	0 N 9	3 S17	23 43	28 26 52	1 S 3
27	F	6 22 33	5 52 3	23 18	5 ♈ 29 5	1 S 5	1 N11	23 39	12 ♈ 28 47	3 N23
28	S	6 26 29	6 49 16	23 16	19 25 53	2 15	5 31	23 36	26 20 25	7 34
29	Su	6 30 26	7 46 29	23 13	3 ♉ 12 22	3 16	9 31	23 33	10 ♉ 1 42	11 19
30	M	6 34 22	8 ♋ 43 42	23 N 9	16 ♉ 48 25	4 S 5	12 N57	23 ♍ 30	23 ♉ 32 27	14 N24

D M	Mercury Lat.	Mercury Dec.	Mercury Dec.	Venus Lat.	Venus Dec.	Venus Dec.	Mars Lat.	Mars Dec.	Mars Dec.	Jupiter Lat.	Jupiter Dec.
	° ′	° ′	° ′	° ′	° ′	° ′	° ′	° ′	° ′	° ′	° ′
1	2 S 48	14 N32	15 N 3	0 N 48	24 N12	24 N15	0 N 53	3 N33	3 N 23	0 S 43	14 S 55
3	2 34	15 33	16 5	0 52	24 18	24 21	0 49	3 13	3 4	0 44	14 54
5	2 17	16 36	17 8	0 57	24 22	24 23	0 46	2 54	2 43	0 44	14 54
7	1 58	17 40	18 12	1 1	24 23	24 23	0 42	2 33	2 23	0 45	14 54
9	1 38	18 44	19 16	1 5	24 21	24 19	0 39	2 12	2 2	0 45	14 55
11	1 17	19 47	20 17	1 8	24 16	24 13	0 36	1 51	1 40	0 46	14 55
13	0 55	20 47	21 16	1 12	24 9	24 4	0 33	1 29	1 18	0 46	14 56
15	0 33	21 43	22 9	1 16	23 58	23 52	0 30	1 7	0 55	0 47	14 57
17	0 S 10	22 34	22 57	1 19	23 45	23 37	0 27	0 44	0 32	0 47	14 58
19	0 N11	23 17	23 36	1 22	23 29	23 20	0 24	0 N21	0 N 9	0 48	15 0
21	0 32	23 52	24 6	1 25	23 10	23 0	0 21	0 S 3	0 S 15	0 48	15 1
23	0 51	24 17	24 26	1 27	22 49	22 37	0 19	0 27	0 39	0 49	15 3
25	1 8	24 32	24 35	1 30	22 25	22 12	0 16	0 51	1 3	0 49	15 6
27	1 23	24 35	24 32	1 32	21 58	21 44	0 13	1 16	1 28	0 50	15 8
29	1 35	24 26	24 N 18	1 33	21 29	21 N13	0 11	1 41	1 S 53	0 50	15 11
31	1 N43	24 N 7		1 N 35	20 N57		0 N 8	2 S 6		0 S 51	15 S 14

FIRST QUARTER-June13, 4h.51m. am. (22°♍14′)

FULL MOON-June20, 7h. 9m. pm. (29°♐29′)

D M	☿ Long.	♀ Long.	♂ Long.	♃ Long.	♄ Long.	♅ Long.	♆ Long.	♇ Long.
	° ′	° ′	° ′	° ′	° ′	° ′	° ′	° ′
1	18♉ 9	26♊43	23♍ 6	21♒49	17♈22	8♒31	29♑43	4♐ 2
2	19 36	27 57	23 26	21 51	17 28	8R 30	29R 42	4R 1
3	21 5	29♊10	23 47	21 52	17 33	8 29	29 41	3 59
4	22 37	0♋24	24 8	21 54	17 38	8 28	29 40	3 57
5	24 11	1 37	24 29	21 54	17 44	8 27	29 39	3 56
6	25 48	2 50	24 51	21 55	17 49	8 26	29 38	3 54
7	27 28	4 4	25 13	21 56	17 54	8 25	29 37	3 52
8	29♉10	5 17	25 35	21 56	17 59	8 24	29 36	3 51
9	0♊55	6 30	25 58	21 56	18 4	8 23	29 35	3 49
10	2 43	7 44	26 21	21R 56	18 9	8 21	29 34	3 48
11	4 33	8 57	26 45	21 56	18 13	8 20	29 32	3 46
12	6 25	10 10	27 8	21 56	18 18	8 19	29 31	3 45
13	8 20	11 24	27 32	21 55	18 23	8 17	29 30	3 43
14	10 17	12 37	27 57	21 55	18 27	8 16	29 29	3 42
15	12 16	13 50	28 22	21 54	18 32	8 14	29 28	3 40
16	14 18	15 3	28 47	21 52	18 36	8 13	29 26	3 39
17	16 21	16 16	29 12	21 51	18 40	8 11	29 25	3 37
18	18 26	17 29	29♍38	21 50	18 45	8 10	29 24	3 36
19	20 33	18 43	0♎ 4	21 48	18 49	8 8	29 23	3 34
20	22 42	19 56	0 30	21 46	18 53	8 6	29 21	3 33
21	24 51	21 9	0 57	21 44	18 57	8 5	29 20	3 31
22	27 2	22 22	1 23	21 42	19 1	8 3	29 18	3 30
23	29♊13	23 35	1 50	21 39	19 5	8 1	29 17	3 28
24	1♋24	24 48	2 18	21 37	19 9	7 59	29 16	3 27
25	3 35	26 1	2 45	21 34	19 12	7 58	29 14	3 26
26	5 46	27 14	3 13	21 31	19 16	7 56	29 13	3 24
27	7 57	28 27	3 41	21 27	19 19	7 54	29 11	3 23
28	10 7	29♋40	4 10	21 24	19 23	7 52	29 10	3 22
29	12 16	0♌53	4 38	21 21	19 26	7 50	29 8	3 20
30	14♋24	2♌ 6	5♎ 7	21♒17	19♈29	7♒48	29♑ 7	3♐19

D M	Lunar Aspects ☉	☿	♀	♂	♃	♄	♅	♆	♇
1	∠	⚺	✱		✱	●			⚼
2	⚺			⚼			□	□	
3		☌	∠	△	□	⚺			
4			⚺			∠	△	△	☍
5	☌				△	✱	⚼	⚼	
6		⚺	☌	□	⚼				
7	⚺	∠				□			⚼
8		✱		✱				☍	
9	∠		⚺	∠			☍		△
10	✱		∠		☍	△			
11		□		⚺		⚼			□
12			✱					⚼	
13	□			●			⚼	△	
14		△	□		⚼		△		✱
15	△				△	☍			∠
16		⚼		⚺			□	□	⚺
17	⚼		△	∠					
18			⚼	✱	□	⚼		✱	☌
19							✱	∠	
20	☍	☍		□	✱	△	∠	⚺	
21					∠		⚺		⚺
22			☍		⚺	□		☌	∠
23		⚼		△			☌		✱
24	⚼			⚼	☌	✱		⚺	
25	△	△	⚼			∠	⚺	∠	□
26			△		⚺	⚺	∠		
27	□	□		☍	∠		✱	✱	△
28					✱	●			⚼
29	✱		□				□	□	
30		✱		⚼	□	⚺			

D M	Saturn Lat.	Saturn Dec.	Uranus Lat.	Uranus Dec.	Neptune Lat.	Neptune Dec.	Pluto Lat.	Pluto Dec.
	° ′	° ′	° ′	° ′	° ′	° ′	° ′	° ′
1	2S18	4N42	0S38	18S44	0N25	19S48	12N56	8S13
3	2 18	4 45	0 38	18 45	0 25	19 48	12 56	8 13
5	2 19	4 49	0 38	18 45	0 25	19 49	12 56	8 13
7	2 19	4 52	0 38	18 46	0 25	19 49	12 56	8 13
9	2 20	4 56	0 38	18 47	0 25	19 49	12 55	8 13
11	2 20	4 59	0 38	18 47	0 25	19 50	12 55	8 12
13	2 21	5 2	0 38	18 48	0 25	19 50	12 54	8 12
15	2 21	5 5	0 38	18 49	0 25	19 51	12 54	8 12
17	2 21	5 8	0 38	18 50	0 25	19 51	12 53	8 12
19	2 22	5 11	0 38	18 51	0 25	19 52	12 53	8 12
21	2 22	5 13	0 38	18 52	0 25	19 53	12 52	8 12
23	2 23	5 16	0 38	18 53	0 25	19 53	12 52	8 12
25	2 23	5 18	0 38	18 54	0 25	19 54	12 51	8 12
27	2 24	5 20	0 38	18 55	0 25	19 54	12 50	8 13
29	2 24	5 23	0 38	18 56	0 25	19 55	12 50	8 13
31	2S25	5N24	0S38	18S57	0N25	19S56	12N49	8S13

Mutual Aspects

2 ♂⚼♅. ☿P♃.
3 ♀Q♄. ♀∇♆.
4 ☿□♃.
5 ☉⚼♆. ☿△♂. ☿⊥♄.
6 ♀±♅. 7 ♀∇♇.
8 ☉✱♄. ☿⊥♀. ☿△♆.
9 ♀⚼♃. ☿P♅.
10 ☿∠♄. ♃Stat.
11 ☿☍♇. ♀∇♅. ☿P♆.
12 ☉△♃. ♀±♇.
13 ☿△♅.
14 ☉⚼♅. ☉±♆. ♂±♃.
16 ☿⚼♆. ♄⚼♇.
17 ☿⚺♀. ♀±♃. ♂△♆.
18 ☿✱♄. ♀Q♂.
19 ♀□♄. ♀⚼♇. ☉P☿. ☉P♀. ☿P♀.
20 ☉∇♆. ☿△♃. ☿⚼♅. ☿±♆.
21 ♀∇♃. 22 ☉Q♄.
23 ☉□♂. ☉±♅. ☿∇♆.
24 ☉∇♇. ☿Q♄. ☿±♅.
25 ☉☌☿. ☿□♂. ☿∇♇.
26 ☿⚼♃. ♂✱♇.
27 ☿∇♅.
28 ☉⚼♃. ☿±♇. ♀☍♆.
29 ☉∇♅. 30 ☿±♃.

LAST QUARTER-June27, 0h.42m. pm. (5°♈54′)

NEW MOON-July 4, 6h.40m. pm. (12°♋48′)

D M	D W	Sidereal Time	☉ Long.	☉ Dec.	☽ Long.	☽ Lat.	☽ Dec.	☽ Node	Midnight ☽ Long.	Midnight ☽ Dec.
		H. M. S.	° ′ ″	° ′	° ′ ″	° ′	° ′	° ′	° ′ ″	° ′
1	T	6 38 19	9 ♋ 40 55	23 N 5	0 ♊ 13 44	4 S 39	15 N39	23 ♍ 27	6 ♊ 52 10	16 N41
2	W	6 42 15	10 38 8	23 1	13 27 38	4 58	17 29	23 23	20 0 1	18 3
3	Th	6 46 12	11 35 22	22 56	26 29 12	5 1	18 22	23 20	2 ♋ 55 5	18 27
4	F	6 50 9	12 32 35	22 51	9 ♋ 17 35	4 49	18 18	23 17	15 36 39	17 56
5	S	6 54 5	13 29 49	22 45	21 52 15	4 23	17 20	23 14	28 4 28	16 32
6	Su	6 58 2	14 27 2	22 39	4 ♌ 13 22	3 45	15 34	23 11	10 ♌ 19 8	14 25
7	M	7 1 58	15 24 16	22 33	16 21 59	2 57	13 7	23 8	22 22 12	11 42
8	T	7 5 55	16 21 29	22 26	28 20 8	2 1	10 9	23 4	4 ♍ 16 12	8 31
9	W	7 9 51	17 18 42	22 19	10 ♍ 10 52	1 S 1	6 48	23 1	16 4 38	5 2
10	Th	7 13 48	18 15 56	22 11	21 58 5	0 N 2	3 N13	22 58	27 51 48	1 N21
11	F	7 17 44	19 13 9	22 4	3 ♎ 46 24	1 4	0 S31	22 55	9 ♎ 42 34	2 S23
12	S	7 21 41	20 10 22	21 55	15 40 57	2 5	4 15	22 52	21 42 14	6 5
13	Su	7 25 38	21 7 35	21 47	27 47 5	3 1	7 52	22 49	3 ♏ 56 8	9 35
14	M	7 29 34	22 4 48	21 38	10 ♏ 10 1	3 50	11 14	22 45	16 29 16	12 45
15	T	7 33 31	23 2 1	21 28	22 54 23	4 29	14 10	22 42	29 25 46	15 24
16	W	7 37 27	23 59 14	21 19	6 ♐ 3 41	4 55	16 28	22 39	12 ♐ 48 18	17 20
17	Th	7 41 24	24 56 28	21 8	19 39 36	5 6	17 57	22 36	26 37 25	18 19
18	F	7 45 20	25 53 42	20 58	3 ♑ 41 26	4 59	18 24	22 33	10 ♑ 51 8	18 12
19	S	7 49 17	26 50 56	20 47	18 5 51	4 33	17 42	22 29	25 24 47	16 54
20	Su	7 53 13	27 48 10	20 36	2 ♒ 47 0	3 49	15 49	22 26	10 ♒ 11 30	14 28
21	M	7 57 10	28 45 25	20 24	17 37 17	2 49	12 52	22 23	25 3 19	11 4
22	T	8 1 7	29 ♋ 42 41	20 13	2 ♓ 28 37	1 37	9 5	22 20	9 ♓ 52 19	6 58
23	W	8 5 3	0 ♌ 39 57	20 0	17 13 38	0 N19	4 45	22 17	24 31 54	2 S29
24	Th	8 9 0	1 37 14	19 48	1 ♈ 46 37	0 S59	0 S12	22 14	8 ♈ 57 24	2 N 4
25	F	8 12 56	2 34 32	19 35	16 3 57	2 12	4 N17	22 10	23 6 9	6 25
26	S	8 16 53	3 31 51	19 22	0 ♉ 3 56	3 16	8 26	22 7	6 ♉ 57 18	10 19
27	Su	8 20 49	4 29 11	19 8	13 46 20	4 7	12 2	22 4	20 31 9	13 35
28	M	8 24 46	5 26 32	18 54	27 11 54	4 44	14 56	22 1	3 ♊ 48 43	16 4
29	T	8 28 42	6 23 55	18 40	10 ♊ 21 45	5 4	16 59	21 58	16 51 11	17 40
30	W	8 32 39	7 21 18	18 26	23 17 10	5 9	18 8	21 54	29 39 48	18 21
31	Th	8 36 36	8 ♌ 18 42	18 N11	5 ♋ 59 15	4 S58	18 N20	21 ♍ 51	12 ♋ 15 37	18 N 6

D M	Mercury Lat.	Mercury Dec.		Venus Lat.	Venus Dec.		Mars Lat.	Mars Dec.		Jupiter Lat.	Jupiter Dec.
	° ′	° ′	° ′	° ′	° ′	° ′	° ′	° ′	° ′	° ′	° ′
1	1 N43	24 N 7	23 N 54	1 N 35	20 N57	20 N41	0 N 8	2 S 6	2 S 19	0 S 51	15 S 14
3	1 49	23 39	23 21	1 36	20 23	20 6	0 6	2 32	2 44	0 51	15 17
5	1 52	23 1	22 39	1 37	19 47	19 28	0 3	2 57	3 10	0 52	15 20
7	1 52	22 16	21 50	1 38	19 9	18 49	0 N 1	3 23	3 37	0 52	15 24
9	1 49	21 24	20 56	1 38	18 29	18 8	0 S 1	3 50	4 3	0 53	15 27
11	1 44	20 26	19 56	1 39	17 46	17 25	0 4	4 16	4 30	0 53	15 31
13	1 36	19 24	18 52	1 38	17 2	16 40	0 6	4 43	4 57	0 54	15 35
15	1 27	18 18	17 44	1 38	16 16	15 53	0 8	5 10	5 24	0 54	15 40
17	1 15	17 10	16 34	1 37	15 29	15 4	0 10	5 37	5 51	0 54	15 44
19	1 2	15 59	15 23	1 36	14 40	14 14	0 12	6 4	6 18	0 55	15 48
21	0 46	14 47	14 11	1 35	13 49	13 23	0 14	6 32	6 45	0 55	15 53
23	0 30	13 34	12 58	1 33	12 57	12 30	0 16	6 59	7 13	0 56	15 58
25	0 N12	12 21	11 45	1 31	12 3	11 36	0 18	7 27	7 41	0 56	16 2
27	0 S 7	11 9	10 33	1 29	11 9	10 41	0 20	7 54	8 8	0 56	16 7
29	0 28	9 57	9 N 22	1 26	10 13	9 N45	0 22	8 22	8 S 36	0 57	16 12
31	0 S49	8 N47		1 N 23	9 N16		0 S 24	8 S50		0 S 57	16 S17

FIRST QUARTER-July12, 9h.44m. pm. (20°♎34′)

FULL MOON-July20, 3h.20m. am. (27°♑28′)

D M	☿ Long.	♀ Long.	♂ Long.	♃ Long.	♄ Long.	♅ Long.	♆ Long.	♇ Long.	Lunar Aspects ☉	☿	♀	♂	♃	♄	♅	♆	♇
	° ′	° ′	° ′	° ′	° ′	° ′	° ′	° ′									
1	16♋31	3♌19	5♎36	21♒13	19♈32	7♒46	29♑ 5	3♐ 18	∠	∠	✱	△		∠		△	☍
2	18 36	4 31	6 5	21R 9	19 35	7R 44	29R 4	3R 17	⚺	⚺				✱	△	⚼	
3	20 40	5 44	6 35	21 5	19 38	7 42	29 2	3 16			∠		△		⚼		
4	22 42	6 57	7 5	21 0	19 41	7 40	29 1	3 14	☌		⚺	□	⚼				
5	24 42	8 10	7 35	20 56	19 44	7 38	28 59	3 13		☌				□			⚼
6	26 40	9 23	8 5	20 51	19 47	7 36	28 58	3 12			☌	✱			☍	☍	△
7	28♋36	10 36	8 35	20 46	19 49	7 33	28 56	3 11	⚺				☍	△			
8	0♌31	11 48	9 6	20 41	19 52	7 31	28 55	3 10	∠	⚺		∠					□
9	2 24	13 1	9 37	20 36	19 54	7 29	28 53	3 9			⚺	⚺		⚼		⚼	
10	4 14	14 14	10 8	20 30	19 56	7 27	28 52	3 8	✱	∠					⚼		
11	6 3	15 26	10 39	20 25	19 59	7 25	28 50	3 7		✱	∠		⚼		△	△	✱
12	7 50	16 39	11 11	20 19	20 1	7 22	28 48	3 6	□		✱	☌	△	☍			∠
13	9 35	17 52	11 42	20 13	20 3	7 20	28 47	3 5								□	⚺
14	11 18	19 4	12 14	20 8	20 5	7 18	28 45	3 4		□		⚺			□		
15	12 59	20 17	12 46	20 2	20 6	7 16	28 43	3 3	△		□	∠	□			✱	
16	14 38	21 29	13 18	19 55	20 8	7 13	28 42	3 2	⚼					⚼	✱		☌
17	16 15	22 42	13 51	19 49	20 10	7 11	28 40	3 1		△	△	✱	✱	△	∠	∠	
18	17 50	23 54	14 23	19 43	20 11	7 9	28 39	3 0		⚼	⚼		∠		⚺	⚺	⚺
19	19 23	25 7	14 56	19 36	20 13	7 6	28 37	3 0				□	⚺	□			∠
20	20 54	26 19	15 29	19 29	20 14	7 4	28 35	2 59	☍						☌	☌	✱
21	22 23	27 32	16 2	19 23	20 15	7 2	28 34	2 58		☍		△	☌	✱			
22	23 51	28 44	16 36	19 16	20 16	6 59	28 32	2 57			☍	⚼		∠	⚺	⚺	□
23	25 16	29♌56	17 9	19 9	20 17	6 57	28 31	2 57	⚼				⚺	⚺	∠	∠	
24	26 39	1♍ 8	17 43	19 2	20 18	6 55	28 29	2 56	△				∠		✱	✱	△
25	28 0	2 21	18 17	18 55	20 19	6 52	28 27	2 55		⚼	⚼	☍	✱	●			⚼
26	29♌19	3 33	18 50	18 47	20 20	6 50	28 26	2 55	□	△	△				□	□	
27	0♍36	4 45	19 25	18 40	20 20	6 47	28 24	2 54					□	⚺			
28	1 51	5 57	19 59	18 33	20 21	6 45	28 22	2 54		□						△	☍
29	3 3	7 9	20 33	18 25	20 21	6 43	28 21	2 53	✱		□	⚼		∠	△	⚼	
30	4 13	8 21	21 8	18 18	20 21	6 40	28 19	2 53	∠			△	△	✱	⚼		
31	5♍21	9♍34	21♎43	18♒10	20♈22	6♒38	28♑18	2♐ 52	⚺	✱	✱		⚼				

D M	Saturn Lat.	Saturn Dec.	Uranus Lat.	Uranus Dec.	Neptune Lat.	Neptune Dec.	Pluto Lat.	Pluto Dec.
	° ′	° ′	° ′	° ′	° ′	° ′	° ′	° ′
1	2S25	5N24	0S38	18S57	0N25	19S56	12N49	8S13
3	2 25	5 26	0 38	18 58	0 25	19 56	12 48	8 13
5	2 26	5 28	0 39	18 59	0 25	19 57	12 48	8 14
7	2 26	5 29	0 39	19 0	0 25	19 58	12 47	8 14
9	2 27	5 31	0 39	19 1	0 25	19 58	12 46	8 14
11	2 28	5 32	0 39	19 2	0 25	19 59	12 45	8 15
13	2 28	5 33	0 39	19 4	0 25	20 0	12 45	8 15
15	2 29	5 34	0 39	19 5	0 25	20 0	12 44	8 16
17	2 29	5 35	0 39	19 6	0 25	20 1	12 43	8 16
19	2 30	5 35	0 39	19 7	0 25	20 2	12 42	8 17
21	2 30	5 36	0 39	19 8	0 25	20 2	12 41	8 17
23	2 31	5 36	0 39	19 10	0 25	20 3	12 40	8 18
25	2 31	5 36	0 39	19 11	0 25	20 4	12 39	8 19
27	2 32	5 36	0 39	19 12	0 25	20 4	12 39	8 19
29	2 33	5 36	0 39	19 13	0 25	20 5	12 38	8 20
31	2S33	5N35	0S39	19S14	0N25	20S 6	12N37	8S21

Mutual Aspects

1 ☉±♇. ♀△♇.
2 ☿□♄. ☿⚼♇. ♂⚼♃.
3 ☿▽♃.
4 ♀✱♂. ♄Q♅. ♀P♆.
5 ♀☍♅. ♂△♅.
6 ☉±♃. ☿Q♂. ☉P☿.
7 ☿☍♆. ♀P♅.
9 ☿△♇. 10 ☉⚼♇.
12 ☉▽♃. ☉□♄. ☿☍♅. ☿P♆.
14 ♃✱♄. ☿P♅.
15 ☿✱♂. ♀☍♃. ♀△♄.
16 ♀P♃. 17 ♂P♄.
19 ☿☍♃. ☿P♃.
20 ☿△♄. 21 ☉☍♆.
22 ♀▽♆.
23 ☉P♆.
24 ♂∠♇.
25 ☉△♇. ☿▽♆. ♀□♇.
26 ☉⚺♀. ♀∠♂. ♂△♃.
27 ♀⚼♄. ♀±♆. ☉P♅. ☿P♀.
29 ☉☍♅. ☿□♇. ♀▽♅. ♂☍♄. ♂P♇.
30 ☿±♆.
31 ☿⚼♄. ☿P♂.

LAST QUARTER-July26, 6h.28m. pm. (3°♉47′)

NEW MOON-Aug. 3, 8h.14m. am. (11° ♌ 2′)

D M	D W	Sidereal Time	☉ Long.	☉ Dec.	☽ Long.	☽ Lat.	☽ Dec.	☽ Node	Midnight ☽ Long.	Midnight ☽ Dec.
		H. M. S.	° ′ ″	° ′	° ′ ″	° ′	° ′	° ′	° ′ ″	° ′
1	F	8 40 32	9 ♌ 16 7	17 N56	18 ♋ 29 2	4 S 33	17 N39	21 ♍ 48	24 ♋ 39 36	16 N59
2	S	8 44 29	10 13 33	17 41	0 ♌ 47 29	3 56	16 8	21 45	6 ♌ 52 47	15 7
3	Su	8 48 25	11 11 0	17 25	12 55 41	3 8	13 55	21 42	18 56 22	12 35
4	M	8 52 22	12 8 28	17 9	24 55 2	2 13	11 8	21 39	0 ♍ 51 56	9 34
5	T	8 56 18	13 5 57	16 53	6 ♍ 47 21	1 12	7 54	21 35	12 41 36	6 11
6	W	9 0 15	14 3 26	16 37	18 35 3	0 S 8	4 24	21 32	24 28 5	2 N34
7	Th	9 4 11	15 0 57	16 20	0 ♎ 21 10	0 N56	0 N43	21 29	6 ♎ 14 46	1 S 8
8	F	9 8 8	15 58 28	16 3	12 9 23	1 58	2 S59	21 26	18 5 34	4 49
9	S	9 12 5	16 56 0	15 46	24 3 55	2 56	6 37	21 23	0 ♏ 4 59	8 21
10	Su	9 16 1	17 53 33	15 28	6 ♏ 9 24	3 46	10 1	21 20	12 17 46	11 35
11	M	9 19 58	18 51 7	15 10	18 30 41	4 28	13 3	21 16	24 48 44	14 22
12	T	9 23 54	19 48 42	14 52	1 ♐ 12 26	4 57	15 33	21 13	7 ♐ 42 16	16 33
13	W	9 27 51	20 46 18	14 34	14 18 38	5 12	17 20	21 10	21 1 49	17 55
14	Th	9 31 47	21 43 55	14 16	27 52 1	5 11	18 14	21 7	4 ♑ 49 14	18 17
15	F	9 35 44	22 41 32	13 57	11 ♑ 53 20	4 52	18 4	21 4	19 4 0	17 33
16	S	9 39 40	23 39 11	13 38	26 20 45	4 13	16 44	21 0	3 ♒ 42 54	15 38
17	Su	9 43 37	24 36 51	13 19	11 ♒ 9 36	3 17	14 16	20 57	18 39 52	12 38
18	M	9 47 34	25 34 32	13 0	26 12 36	2 6	10 48	20 54	3 ♓ 46 40	8 46
19	T	9 51 30	26 32 15	12 40	11 ♓ 20 53	0 N47	6 35	20 51	18 54 4	4 S19
20	W	9 55 27	27 29 58	12 20	26 25 9	0 S36	1 S59	20 48	3 ♈ 53 10	0 N22
21	Th	9 59 23	28 27 44	12 0	11 ♈ 17 14	1 56	2 N41	20 45	18 36 40	4 56
22	F	10 3 20	29 ♌ 25 31	11 40	25 50 54	3 6	7 6	20 41	2 ♉ 59 35	9 7
23	S	10 7 16	0 ♍ 23 19	11 20	10 ♉ 2 27	4 3	10 58	20 38	16 59 25	12 39
24	Su	10 11 13	1 21 10	11 0	23 50 28	4 44	14 8	20 35	0 ♊ 35 45	15 24
25	M	10 15 9	2 19 2	10 39	7 ♊ 15 27	5 9	16 26	20 32	13 49 48	17 15
26	T	10 19 6	3 16 56	10 18	20 19 9	5 16	17 49	20 29	26 43 47	18 10
27	W	10 23 3	4 14 52	9 57	3 ♋ 4 6	5 8	18 16	20 26	9 ♋ 20 25	18 9
28	Th	10 26 59	5 12 50	9 36	15 33 7	4 45	17 48	20 22	21 42 32	17 16
29	F	10 30 56	6 10 49	9 15	27 49 0	4 10	16 31	20 19	3 ♌ 52 52	15 35
30	S	10 34 52	7 8 50	8 53	9 ♌ 54 26	3 23	14 30	20 16	15 54 0	13 15
31	Su	10 38 49	8 ♍ 6 53	8 N32	21 ♌ 51 50	2 S28	11 N53	20 ♍ 13	27 ♌ 48 14	10 N23

D M	Mercury Lat.	Mercury Dec.		Venus Lat.	Venus Dec.		Mars Lat.	Mars Dec.		Jupiter Lat.	Jupiter Dec.
	° ′	° ′	° ′	° ′	° ′	° ′	° ′	° ′	° ′	° ′	° ′
1	1 S 0	8 N13	7 N 40	1 N 21	8 N47	8 N18	0 S 25	9 S 4	9 S 18	0 S 57	16 S 20
3	1 22	7 7	6 36	1 18	7 49	7 20	0 27	9 31	9 45	0 57	16 25
5	1 45	6 5	5 35	1 14	6 50	6 20	0 28	9 59	10 13	0 58	16 30
7	2 8	5 6	4 38	1 10	5 51	5 20	0 30	10 27	10 41	0 58	16 35
9	2 32	4 12	3 47	1 6	4 50	4 20	0 32	10 55	11 8	0 58	16 40
11	2 54	3 24	3 3	1 1	3 50	3 19	0 33	11 22	11 36	0 59	16 45
13	3 17	2 43	2 26	0 57	2 48	2 18	0 35	11 50	12 3	0 59	16 50
15	3 38	2 11	1 58	0 51	1 47	1 16	0 36	12 17	12 31	0 59	16 54
17	3 57	1 48	1 40	0 46	0 N45	0 N14	0 38	12 44	12 58	0 59	16 59
19	4 13	1 35	1 34	0 40	0 S17	0 S48	0 40	13 12	13 25	0 59	17 4
21	4 26	1 35	1 40	0 34	1 19	1 50	0 41	13 38	13 52	0 59	17 9
23	4 35	1 48	1 59	0 28	2 21	2 51	0 42	14 5	14 19	1 0	17 13
25	4 37	2 14	2 32	0 22	3 22	3 53	0 44	14 32	14 45	1 0	17 17
27	4 33	2 54	3 18	0 15	4 24	4 55	0 45	14 58	15 11	1 0	17 22
29	4 21	3 45	4 N 14	0 8	5 25	5 S56	0 47	15 24	15 S 37	1 0	17 26
31	4 S 1	4 N45		0 N 2	6 S26		0 S 48	15 S 50		1 S 0	17 S 30

FIRST QUARTER-Aug.11, 0h.42m. pm. (18° ♏ 53′)

FULL MOON-Aug.18,10h.55m. am. (25°♒32′)

EPHEMERIS]			AUGUST 1997														17
D	☿	♀	♂	♃	♄	♅	♆	♇	Lunar Aspects								
M	Long.	Long.	Long.	Long.	Long.	Long.	Long.	Long.	☉	☿	♀	♂	♃	♄	♅	♆	♇
	° ′	° ′	° ′	° ′	° ′	° ′	° ′	° ′									
1	6♍26	10♍46	22♎18	18♒ 3	20♈22	6♒35	28♑16	2♐ 52		∠		□		□			⚼
2	7 28	11 58	22 53	17R 55	20R 22	6R 33	28R 14	2R 52			∠				☍	☍	△
3	8 28	13 9	23 28	17 47	20 21	6 31	28 13	2 51	☌	⚺	⚺		☍				
4	9 25	14 21	24 3	17 40	20 21	6 28	28 11	2 51				✱		△			
5	10 19	15 33	24 39	17 32	20 21	6 26	28 10	2 51		●		∠		⚼			□
6	11 10	16 45	25 15	17 24	20 20	6 23	28 8	2 50	⚺		☌				⚼	⚼	
7	11 57	17 57	25 50	17 16	20 20	6 21	28 7	2 50	∠			⚺	⚼			△	✱
8	12 42	19 9	26 26	17 8	20 19	6 19	28 5	2 50	✱	⚺			△		△		∠
9	13 22	20 20	27 2	17 1	20 18	6 16	28 4	2 50		∠	⚺	☌		☍		□	
10	13 59	21 32	27 39	16 53	20 18	6 14	28 2	2 50			∠				□		⚺
11	14 32	22 44	28 15	16 45	20 17	6 12	28 1	2 50	□	✱	✱		□				
12	15 1	23 55	28 52	16 37	20 16	6 9	27 59	2 50				⚺		⚼	✱	✱	☌
13	15 25	25 7	29♎28	16 29	20 14	6 7	27 58	2D 50		□		∠	✱	△		∠	
14	15 45	26 18	0♏ 5	16 21	20 13	6 5	27 56	2 50	△		□	✱	∠		∠	⚺	⚺
15	15 59	27 30	0 42	16 14	20 12	6 3	27 55	2 50	⚼	△			⚺		⚺		∠
16	16 9	28 41	1 19	16 6	20 10	6 0	27 53	2 50		⚼	△	□		□		☌	✱
17	16 14	29♍53	1 56	15 58	20 9	5 58	27 52	2 50			⚼		☌		☌		
18	16R 13	1♎ 4	2 34	15 51	20 7	5 56	27 51	2 50	☍			△		✱		⚺	□
19	16 6	2 15	3 11	15 43	20 5	5 54	27 49	2 50		☍		⚼	⚺	∠	⚺	∠	
20	15 54	3 26	3 48	15 36	20 4	5 51	27 48	2 50					∠	⚺	∠	✱	△
21	15 36	4 37	4 26	15 28	20 2	5 49	27 46	2 51	⚼		☍		✱		✱		⚼
22	15 12	5 48	5 4	15 21	20 0	5 47	27 45	2 51	△	⚼				●		□	
23	14 42	7 0	5 42	15 13	19 57	5 45	27 44	2 51		△		☍	□		□		
24	14 7	8 10	6 20	15 6	19 55	5 43	27 42	2 52			⚼			⚺		△	
25	13 27	9 21	6 58	14 59	19 53	5 41	27 41	2 52	□	□	△			∠	△	⚼	☍
26	12 43	10 32	7 36	14 52	19 51	5 39	27 40	2 52				⚼	△	✱	⚼		
27	11 54	11 43	8 15	14 45	19 48	5 37	27 39	2 53	✱			△	⚼				
28	11 2	12 54	8 53	14 38	19 45	5 35	27 38	2 53	∠	✱	□			□			⚼
29	10 7	14 5	9 32	14 31	19 43	5 33	27 36	2 54		∠						☍	△
30	9 11	15 15	10 11	14 25	19 40	5 31	27 35	2 55	⚺	⚺	✱	□	☍		☍		
31	8♍15	16♎26	10♏50	14♒18	19♈37	5♒29	27♑34	2♐ 55						△			

D	Saturn		Uranus		Neptune		Pluto	
M	Lat.	Dec.	Lat.	Dec.	Lat.	Dec.	Lat.	Dec.
	° ′	° ′	° ′	° ′	° ′	° ′	° ′	° ′
1	2S33	5N35	0S39	19S15	0N25	20S 6	12N36	8S21
3	2 34	5 35	0 39	19 16	0 25	20 7	12 35	8 22
5	2 34	5 34	0 39	19 17	0 25	20 7	12 34	8 23
7	2 35	5 33	0 39	19 19	0 25	20 8	12 33	8 24
9	2 36	5 32	0 39	19 20	0 25	20 9	12 32	8 25
11	2 36	5 31	0 39	19 21	0 25	20 9	12 31	8 25
13	2 37	5 29	0 39	19 22	0 25	20 10	12 30	8 26
15	2 37	5 28	0 39	19 23	0 25	20 10	12 29	8 27
17	2 38	5 26	0 39	19 24	0 25	20 11	12 28	8 28
19	2 38	5 25	0 39	19 25	0 25	20 12	12 27	8 29
21	2 39	5 23	0 39	19 27	0 25	20 12	12 26	8 31
23	2 39	5 21	0 39	19 28	0 25	20 13	12 25	8 32
25	2 40	5 19	0 39	19 29	0 25	20 13	12 24	8 33
27	2 40	5 16	0 39	19 30	0 24	20 14	12 23	8 34
29	2 41	5 14	0 39	19 30	0 24	20 14	12 22	8 35
31	2S41	5N11	0S39	19S31	0N24	20S15	12N21	8S36

Mutual Aspects

1 ☿⚻♅. ☿P♇. ♀P♂. ♄Stat.
2 ♀±♅. ♀P♇.
3 ☿∠♂. ♀⚼♆.
4 ☉Q♂. ♀±♄.
6 ♀⚻♃. ☉P♃. ☿P♄.
7 ☿±♅. 8 ♀P♄.
9 ☉☍♃. ☿⚼♆. ♀⚻♄. ♀Q♇. ♂⊥♇.
10 ♀⊥♂. ♀⚼♅.
11 ☿±♄. ♀±♃. ♂□♆.
12 ☉△♄.
13 ☿P♀. ♇Stat.
15 ♀△♆.
16 ☿∠♂. ☿⚻♃.
17 ☿Stat.
18 ♀⚼♃. ♂⚺♇. ☉P♂.
19 ♀✱♇.
20 ☉⊥♀. ☉⚻♆.
21 ♀⚺♂.
22 ☿⚻♃. ♀△♅. ☿P♀.
23 ♂□♅. 24 ☿±♄.
26 ☉±♆. ☉□♇. ☿⚼♆. ♃Q♇.
27 ☿⚺♀. ☿±♅.
28 ☉⚼♄. ☉⚻♅.
29 ☿✱♂. ♀△♃. ♀P♄.
30 ☿⊥♀.
31 ☉☌☿. ☉P♇.

LAST QUARTER-Aug.25, 2h.24m. am. (1°♊56′)

NEW MOON-Sep. 1,11h.52m. pm. (9°♍34′)

D M	D W	Sidereal Time	☉ Long.	☉ Dec.	☽ Long.	☽ Lat.	☽ Dec.	☽ Node	Midnight ☽ Long.	Midnight ☽ Dec.
		H. M. S.	° ′ ″	° ′	° ′ ″	° ′	° ′	° ′	° ′ ″	° ′
1	M	10 42 45	9♍ 4 58	8 N10	3♍43 28	1 S28	8 N47	20♍10	9♍37 48	7 N 6
2	T	10 46 42	10 3 4	7 48	15 31 31	0 S23	5 21	20 6	21 24 54	3 N33
3	W	10 50 38	11 1 12	7 26	27 18 13	0 N42	1 N43	20 3	3♎11 47	0 S 8
4	Th	10 54 35	11 59 21	7 4	9♎ 5 57	1 46	1 S59	20 0	15 1 2	3 49
5	F	10 58 32	12 57 32	6 42	20 57 24	2 45	5 37	19 57	26 55 27	7 23
6	S	11 2 28	13 55 45	6 19	2♏55 36	3 38	9 4	19 54	8♏58 18	10 40
7	Su	11 6 25	14 53 59	5 57	15 3 58	4 22	12 11	19 51	21 13 7	13 34
8	M	11 10 21	15 52 15	5 34	27 26 13	4 54	14 48	19 47	3♐43 44	15 53
9	T	11 14 18	16 50 32	5 12	10♐ 6 8	5 14	16 47	19 44	16 33 54	17 29
10	W	11 18 14	17 48 51	4 49	23 7 25	5 18	17 58	19 41	29 47 2	18 13
11	Th	11 22 11	18 47 11	4 26	6♑33 3	5 5	18 12	19 38	13♑25 38	17 56
12	F	11 26 7	19 45 33	4 3	20 24 52	4 34	17 22	19 35	27 30 40	16 32
13	S	11 30 4	20 43 56	3 40	4♒42 49	3 45	15 26	19 32	12♒ 0 55	14 4
14	Su	11 34 1	21 42 21	3 17	19 24 26	2 41	12 27	19 28	26 52 36	10 37
15	M	11 37 57	22 40 48	2 54	4♓24 33	1 24	8 35	19 25	11♓59 14	6 24
16	T	11 41 54	23 39 16	2 31	19 35 32	0 N 1	4 S 6	19 22	27 12 14	1 S45
17	W	11 45 50	24 37 46	2 8	4♈48 7	1 S23	0 N38	19 19	12♈21 59	3 N 0
18	Th	11 49 47	25 36 19	1 45	19 52 42	2 40	5 18	19 16	27 19 16	7 30
19	F	11 53 43	26 34 53	1 22	4♉40 47	3 45	9 33	19 12	11♉56 34	11 26
20	S	11 57 40	27 33 29	0 58	19 6 3	4 34	13 6	19 9	26 8 55	14 34
21	Su	12 1 36	28 32 8	0 35	3♊ 4 57	5 4	15 47	19 6	9♊54 9	16 46
22	M	12 5 33	29♍30 49	0 N12	16 36 36	5 17	17 30	19 3	23 12 33	17 59
23	T	12 9 30	0♎29 32	0 S12	29 42 20	5 13	18 13	19 0	6♋ 6 21	18 13
24	W	12 13 26	1 28 18	0 35	12♋25 4	4 53	18 0	18 57	18 38 59	17 33
25	Th	12 17 23	2 27 5	0 58	24 48 36	4 20	16 54	18 53	0♌54 29	16 4
26	F	12 21 19	3 25 55	1 22	6♌57 8	3 36	15 3	18 50	12 57 5	13 53
27	S	12 25 16	4 24 47	1 45	18 54 50	2 43	12 34	18 47	24 50 51	11 8
28	Su	12 29 12	5 23 42	2 9	0♍45 35	1 44	9 35	18 44	6♍39 27	7 57
29	M	12 33 9	6 22 38	2 32	12 32 51	0 S40	6 14	18 41	18 26 9	4 28
30	T	12 37 5	7♎21 36	2 S55	24♍19 40	0 N25	2 N38	18♍38	0♎13 43	0 N47

D M	Mercury Lat.	Mercury Dec.	Mercury Dec.	Venus Lat.	Venus Dec.	Venus Dec.	Mars Lat.	Mars Dec.	Mars Dec.	Jupiter Lat.	Jupiter Dec.
	° ′	° ′	° ′	° ′	° ′	° ′	° ′	° ′	° ′	° ′	° ′
1	3 S49	5 N17	5 N49	0 S 2	6 S56	7 S27	0 S49	16 S 3	16 S15	1 S 0	17 S31
3	3 19	6 22	6 54	0 9	7 57	8 27	0 50	16 28	16 40	1 0	17 35
5	2 44	7 25	7 55	0 17	8 56	9 26	0 51	16 53	17 5	1 0	17 39
7	2 7	8 22	8 46	0 24	9 55	10 24	0 52	17 17	17 30	1 0	17 42
9	1 28	9 8	9 26	0 32	10 53	11 22	0 53	17 42	17 53	1 0	17 45
11	0 50	9 40	9 51	0 39	11 50	12 19	0 55	18 5	18 17	1 0	17 48
13	0 S15	9 57	10 0	0 47	12 47	13 15	0 56	18 29	18 40	1 0	17 51
15	0 N17	9 58	9 52	0 55	13 42	14 9	0 57	18 51	19 3	1 0	17 53
17	0 44	9 42	9 29	1 3	14 36	15 3	0 58	19 14	19 25	1 0	17 55
19	1 7	9 11	8 50	1 11	15 29	15 55	0 59	19 36	19 46	1 0	17 57
21	1 25	8 26	7 58	1 19	16 20	16 46	1 0	19 57	20 7	0 59	17 59
23	1 38	7 28	6 55	1 27	17 10	17 35	1 1	20 18	20 28	0 59	18 1
25	1 47	6 19	5 42	1 35	17 59	18 23	1 2	20 38	20 48	0 59	18 2
27	1 52	5 3	4 22	1 43	18 46	19 9	1 3	20 57	21 7	0 59	18 4
29	1 53	3 40	2 N 57	1 51	19 31	19 S53	1 4	21 16	21 S 25	0 59	18 5
31	1 N51	2 N14		1 S 58	20 S 15		1 S 4	21 S 34		0 S 59	18 S 5

FIRST QUARTER-Sep.10, 1h.31m. am. (17°♐23′)

FULL MOON-Sep.16, 6h.50m. pm. (23°♓56′)

D M	☿ Long.	♀ Long.	♂ Long.	♃ Long.	♄ Long.	♅ Long.	♆ Long.	♇ Long.	☉	☿	♀	♂	♃	♄	♅	♆	♇
	° ′	° ′	° ′	° ′	° ′	° ′	° ′	° ′									
1	7♍20	17♎36	11♏29	14♒12	19♈34	5♒27	27♑33	2♐ 56	☌	☌	∠			⚼			□
2	6R 26	18 47	12 8	14R 5	19R 31	5R 25	27R 32	2 56			⚺	⚹			⚼	⚼	
3	5 36	19 57	12 47	13 59	19 28	5 23	27 31	2 57				∠	⚼			△	⚹
4	4 51	21 8	13 26	13 53	19 25	5 22	27 30	2 58	⚺	⚺		⚺	△		△		
5	4 11	22 18	14 6	13 47	19 22	5 20	27 29	2 59		∠	☌			☍			∠
6	3 37	23 28	14 45	13 41	19 18	5 18	27 28	2 59	∠	⚹					□	□	⚺
7	3 11	24 38	15 25	13 36	19 15	5 17	27 27	3 0	⚹			☌	□				
8	2 53	25 49	16 5	13 30	19 11	5 15	27 26	3 1		□	⚺					⚹	☌
9	2 44	26 59	16 45	13 25	19 8	5 13	27 25	3 2			∠		⚹	⚼	⚹	∠	
10	2D 43	28 9	17 25	13 19	19 4	5 12	27 24	3 3	□		⚹	⚺	∠	△	∠	⚺	
11	2 51	29♎18	18 5	13 14	19 1	5 10	27 23	3 4		△		∠	⚺		⚺		⚺
12	3 9	0♏28	18 45	13 10	18 57	5 9	27 22	3 5	△	⚼		⚹		□		☌	∠
13	3 36	1 38	19 25	13 5	18 53	5 7	27 21	3 6	⚼		□				☌		⚹
14	4 11	2 48	20 6	13 0	18 49	5 6	27 21	3 7				□	☌	⚹			
15	4 55	3 57	20 46	12 56	18 45	5 5	27 20	3 8		☍	△			∠	⚺	⚺	□
16	5 47	5 7	21 27	12 52	18 41	5 3	27 19	3 9	☍		⚼	△	⚺	⚺	∠	∠	
17	6 47	6 16	22 8	12 48	18 37	5 2	27 18	3 10				⚼	∠		⚹	⚹	△
18	7 54	7 25	22 48	12 44	18 33	5 1	27 18	3 11		⚼			⚹	☌		□	⚼
19	9 7	8 34	23 29	12 40	18 29	4 59	27 17	3 12		△	☍				□		
20	10 26	9 44	24 10	12 36	18 25	4 58	27 16	3 14	⚼			☍	□	⚺			
21	11 51	10 53	24 51	12 33	18 20	4 57	27 16	3 15	△					∠	△	△	☍
22	13 20	12 2	25 33	12 30	18 16	4 56	27 15	3 16		□			△	⚹	⚼	⚼	
23	14 53	13 10	26 14	12 27	18 12	4 55	27 15	3 17	□		⚼		⚼				
24	16 30	14 19	26 55	12 24	18 7	4 54	27 14	3 19		⚹	△	⚼		□			⚼
25	18 9	15 28	27 37	12 22	18 3	4 53	27 14	3 20				△				☍	
26	19 51	16 36	28 18	12 19	17 58	4 52	27 13	3 22	⚹	∠			☍		☍		△
27	21 34	17 45	29 0	12 17	17 54	4 51	27 13	3 23	∠	⚺	□			△			
28	23 20	18 53	29♏42	12 15	17 49	4 51	27 13	3 24	⚺			□		⚼			□
29	25 6	20 1	0♐ 24	12 13	17 45	4 50	27 12	3 26								⚼	
30	26♍53	21♏ 9	1♐ 6	12♒11	17♈40	4♒49	27♑12	3♐ 27		☌	⚹		⚼		⚼	△	

D M	Saturn Lat.	Saturn Dec.	Uranus Lat.	Uranus Dec.	Neptune Lat.	Neptune Dec.	Pluto Lat.	Pluto Dec.
	° ′	° ′	° ′	° ′	° ′	° ′	° ′	° ′
1	2S41	5N10	0S39	19S32	0N24	20S15	12N21	8S37
3	2 42	5 7	0 39	19 33	0 24	20 16	12 20	8 38
5	2 42	5 5	0 39	19 34	0 24	20 16	12 19	8 39
7	2 42	5 2	0 39	19 34	0 24	20 16	12 18	8 41
9	2 43	4 59	0 39	19 35	0 24	20 17	12 17	8 42
11	2 43	4 56	0 39	19 36	0 24	20 17	12 16	8 43
13	2 43	4 52	0 39	19 36	0 24	20 18	12 15	8 44
15	2 44	4 49	0 38	19 37	0 24	20 18	12 14	8 46
17	2 44	4 46	0 38	19 38	0 24	20 18	12 13	8 47
19	2 44	4 43	0 38	19 38	0 24	20 19	12 12	8 48
21	2 45	4 39	0 38	19 39	0 24	20 19	12 11	8 50
23	2 45	4 36	0 38	19 39	0 24	20 19	12 11	8 51
25	2 45	4 32	0 38	19 40	0 24	20 19	12 10	8 52
27	2 45	4 28	0 38	19 40	0 24	20 19	12 9	8 54
29	2 45	4 25	0 38	19 40	0 24	20 20	12 8	8 55
31	2S45	4N21	0S38	19S41	0N24	20S20	12N 7	8S56

Mutual Aspects

1 ♀∠♇. ☿P♄.
2 ☉P♀.
3 ☉±♅. ☿∠♀. ☿⚻♅. ♀☍♄.
4 ☉P☿. ♀P♇.
5 ☉±♄. ☉⚼♆. ☿⚼♄. ♂□♃.
6 ☉⚻♃. ☿±♆.
7 ☿Q♂. ♂Q♆.
8 ☿□♇. ☿P♇.
9 ☉⚹♂. ♀□♆. ♀⊥♇. ♂P♃.
10 ☉P♄. ☿Stat.
11 ☉±♃. ☉⚻♄.
12 ☉⚼♅. ☿□♇. ♂⚻♄.
13 ☉Q♇. ☿⚼♄. ☿±♆.
14 ♀⚺♇. 15 ☿⚻♅.
16 ♀□♅.
18 ♂Q♅.
19 ♂P♅.
20 ☉⚼♃. ☉△♆. ☿±♅. ♂±♄. ☿P♇.
21 ☿⚻♃. ☿±♄. ☿⚼♆.
22 ☿Q♂. ♀□♃. ♄⚼♇.
23 ♂P♆. 24 ♂⚹♆.
25 ☿±♃. ☿⚻♄. ♀Q♆. ♀P♃.
26 ☉⚹♇. ☿⚼♅.
27 ☉△♅. ☿Q♇. ♀⚻♄.
28 ☿P♄.
29 ♂Q♃. ♀P♅.
30 ☿⚼♃. ☿△♆. ☉P☿.

LAST QUARTER-Sep.23, 1h.35m. pm. (0°♋33′)

NEW MOON-Oct. 1, 4h.52m. pm. (8°♎33′) & Oct.31,10h. 1m. am. (8°♏ 1′)

D M	D W	Sidereal Time	☉ Long.	☉ Dec.	☽ Long.	☽ Lat.	☽ Dec.	☽ Node	Midnight ☽ Long.	Midnight ☽ Dec.
		H. M. S.	° ′ ″	° ′	° ′ ″	° ′	° ′	° ′	° ′ ″	° ′
1	W	12 41 2	8♎20 37	3 S 19	6♎ 8 35	1 N29	1 S 4	18♍34	12♎ 4 32	2 S 56
2	Th	12 44 59	9 19 40	3 42	18 1 50	2 30	4 46	18 31	24 0 42	6 33
3	F	12 48 55	10 18 44	4 5	0♏ 1 22	3 24	8 17	18 28	6♏ 4 5	9 57
4	S	12 52 52	11 17 51	4 28	12 9 5	4 10	11 30	18 25	18 16 36	12 57
5	Su	12 56 48	12 16 59	4 51	24 26 53	4 45	14 16	18 22	0♐ 40 12	15 26
6	M	13 0 45	13 16 10	5 14	6♐ 56 49	5 7	16 25	18 18	13 17 2	17 13
7	T	13 4 41	14 15 22	5 37	19 41 9	5 15	17 49	18 15	26 9 27	18 11
8	W	13 8 38	15 14 36	6 0	2♑ 42 14	5 6	18 18	18 12	9♑ 19 47	18 11
9	Th	13 12 34	16 13 52	6 23	16 2 22	4 41	17 49	18 9	22 50 11	17 11
10	F	13 16 31	17 13 9	6 46	29 43 26	4 0	16 17	18 6	6♒ 42 11	15 9
11	S	13 20 28	18 12 28	7 8	13♒ 46 26	3 4	13 45	18 3	20 56 5	12 8
12	Su	13 24 24	19 11 49	7 31	28 10 53	1 54	10 19	17 59	5♓ 30 27	8 19
13	M	13 28 21	20 11 12	7 53	12♓ 54 15	0 N36	6 9	17 56	20 21 35	3 S 53
14	T	13 32 17	21 10 37	8 16	27 51 37	0 S 46	1 S 33	17 53	5♈ 23 23	0 N49
15	W	13 36 14	22 10 3	8 38	12♈ 55 48	2 5	3 N11	17 50	20 27 44	5 30
16	Th	13 40 10	23 9 31	9 0	27 58 2	3 15	7 43	17 47	5♉ 25 33	9 47
17	F	13 44 7	24 9 2	9 22	12♉ 49 13	4 11	11 42	17 43	20 8 5	13 24
18	S	13 48 3	25 8 34	9 44	27 21 20	4 49	14 52	17 40	4♊ 28 19	16 6
19	Su	13 52 0	26 8 9	10 5	11♊ 28 37	5 9	17 3	17 37	18 21 55	17 45
20	M	13 55 57	27 7 46	10 27	25 8 9	5 10	18 11	17 34	1♋ 47 23	18 22
21	T	13 59 53	28 7 26	10 48	8♋ 19 49	4 54	18 17	17 31	14 45 50	17 58
22	W	14 3 50	29♎ 7 7	11 10	21 5 51	4 24	17 26	17 28	27 20 23	16 41
23	Th	14 7 46	0♏ 6 51	11 31	3♌ 30 2	3 43	15 46	17 24	9♌ 35 25	14 40
24	F	14 11 43	1 6 37	11 52	15 37 10	2 52	13 25	17 21	21 35 55	12 2
25	S	14 15 39	2 6 26	12 12	27 32 21	1 54	10 32	17 18	3♍ 27 4	8 56
26	Su	14 19 36	3 6 16	12 33	9♍ 20 40	0 S 52	7 15	17 15	15 13 45	5 30
27	M	14 23 32	4 6 9	12 53	21 6 51	0 N11	3 N42	17 12	27 0 28	1 N51
28	T	14 27 29	5 6 3	13 13	2♎ 55 2	1 14	0 S 1	17 9	8♎ 50 59	1 S 54
29	W	14 31 26	6 6 0	13 33	14 48 38	2 15	3 46	17 5	20 48 20	5 36
30	Th	14 35 22	7 5 59	13 53	26 50 18	3 10	7 24	17 2	2♏ 54 45	9 7
31	F	14 39 19	8♏ 6 0	14 S 12	9♏ 1 52	3 N56	10 S 46	16♍59	15♏ 11 45	12 S 18

D M	Mercury Lat.	Mercury Dec.		Venus Lat.	Venus Dec.		Mars Lat.	Mars Dec.		Jupiter Lat.	Jupiter Dec.
	° ′	° ′	° ′	° ′	° ′	° ′	° ′	° ′	° ′	° ′	° ′
1	1 N51	2 N14	1 N 29	1 S 58	20 S 15	20 S 36	1 S 4	21 S 34	21 S 43	0 S 59	18 S 5
3	1 47	0 N44	0 S 2	2 6	20 56	21 17	1 5	21 52	22 0	0 59	18 6
5	1 40	0 S 48	1 34	2 13	21 36	21 55	1 6	22 8	22 17	0 59	18 6
7	1 32	2 20	3 5	2 21	22 14	22 32	1 7	22 24	22 32	0 58	18 6
9	1 23	3 51	4 37	2 28	22 50	23 7	1 7	22 40	22 47	0 58	18 6
11	1 12	5 22	6 7	2 35	23 23	23 39	1 8	22 54	23 1	0 58	18 5
13	1 0	6 51	7 35	2 42	23 54	24 9	1 9	23 8	23 14	0 58	18 5
15	0 48	8 19	9 2	2 48	24 23	24 37	1 9	23 21	23 27	0 58	18 4
17	0 35	9 45	10 26	2 54	24 50	25 3	1 10	23 32	23 38	0 58	18 3
19	0 22	11 8	11 48	3 0	25 14	25 26	1 11	23 43	23 49	0 57	18 2
21	0 N 8	12 28	13 8	3 6	25 36	25 46	1 11	23 54	23 58	0 57	18 0
23	0 S 5	13 46	14 24	3 11	25 56	26 4	1 12	24 3	24 7	0 57	17 58
25	0 19	15 1	15 37	3 16	26 12	26 20	1 12	24 11	24 15	0 57	17 56
27	0 32	16 12	16 47	3 20	26 27	26 33	1 13	24 18	24 22	0 57	17 54
29	0 46	17 21	17 S 54	3 24	26 39	26 S 43	1 13	24 25	24 S 27	0 56	17 52
31	0 S 59	18 S 25		3 S 27	26 S 48		1 S 13	24 S 30		0 S 56	17 S 49

FIRST QUARTER-Oct. 9, 0h.22m. pm. (16°♑15′)

FULL MOON-Oct.16, 3h.46m. am. (22°♈49′)

D M	☿ Long.	♀ Long.	♂ Long.	♃ Long.	♄ Long.	♅ Long.	♆ Long.	♇ Long.
	° ′	° ′	° ′	° ′	° ′	° ′	° ′	° ′
1	28♍41	22♏17	1♐48	12♒10	17♈35	4♒48	27♑12	3♐29
2	0♎29	23 25	2 30	12R 9	17R 31	4R 48	27R 12	3 31
3	2 17	24 33	3 12	12 8	17 26	4 47	27 11	3 32
4	4 4	25 41	3 55	12 7	17 21	4 47	27 11	3 34
5	5 52	26 48	4 37	12 6	17 17	4 46	27 11	3 35
6	7 39	27 56	5 20	12 6	17 12	4 46	27 11	3 37
7	9 26	29♏ 3	6 2	12 6	17 7	4 45	27 11	3 39
8	11 13	0♐10	6 45	12D 6	17 2	4 45	27 11	3 40
9	12 58	1 17	7 28	12 6	16 58	4 45	27D 11	3 42
10	14 43	2 24	8 10	12 6	16 53	4 45	27 11	3 44
11	16 28	3 30	8 53	12 7	16 48	4 44	27 11	3 46
12	18 12	4 37	9 36	12 7	16 43	4 44	27 11	3 48
13	19 55	5 43	10 20	12 8	16 39	4 44	27 11	3 49
14	21 37	6 49	11 3	12 10	16 34	4D 44	27 11	3 51
15	23 19	7 55	11 46	12 11	16 29	4 44	27 12	3 53
16	25 0	9 1	12 29	12 12	16 25	4 44	27 12	3 55
17	26 41	10 7	13 13	12 14	16 20	4 44	27 12	3 57
18	28 20	11 12	13 56	12 16	16 15	4 45	27 12	3 59
19	29♎59	12 17	14 40	12 18	16 11	4 45	27 13	4 1
20	1♏38	13 22	15 23	12 21	16 6	4 45	27 13	4 3
21	3 16	14 27	16 7	12 23	16 1	4 45	27 13	4 5
22	4 53	15 31	16 51	12 26	15 57	4 46	27 14	4 7
23	6 30	16 36	17 35	12 29	15 52	4 46	27 14	4 9
24	8 6	17 40	18 19	12 32	15 48	4 47	27 15	4 11
25	9 41	18 44	19 3	12 35	15 43	4 47	27 15	4 13
26	11 16	19 47	19 47	12 39	15 39	4 48	27 16	4 15
27	12 51	20 51	20 31	12 42	15 35	4 49	27 16	4 17
28	14 25	21 54	21 15	12 46	15 30	4 49	27 17	4 19
29	15 58	22 57	22 0	12 50	15 26	4 50	27 18	4 21
30	17 31	23 59	22 44	12 54	15 22	4 51	27 18	4 24
31	19♏ 4	25♐ 1	23♐29	12♒59	15♈18	4♒52	27♑19	4♐26

Lunar Aspects

D	☉	☿	♀	♂	♃	♄	♅	♆	♇
1	☌		∠	✱			△		✱
2			⚺	∠	△	☍			∠
3		⚺		⚺			□	□	⚺
4	⚺				□				
5	∠	∠	☌					✱	
6		✱		☌	✱	⚼	✱	∠	☌
7	✱					△	∠		
8			⚺	⚺	∠		⚺	⚺	⚺
9	□	□	∠	∠	⚺	□			∠
10			✱				☌	☌	✱
11	△	△		✱	☌	✱			
12	⚼	⚼	□			∠	⚺	⚺	□
13				□	⚺	⚺	∠	∠	
14					∠		✱	✱	△
15			△	△	✱	●			⚼
16	☍	☍	⚼	⚼			□	□	
17					□	⚺			
18						∠		△	☍
19	⚼	⚼	☍	☍	△	✱	△	⚼	
20	△				⚼		⚼		
21		△							
22						□		☍	⚼
23	□	□	⚼	⚼			☍		△
24			△	△	☍	△			
25	✱					⚼			
26		✱						⚼	□
27	∠		□	□			⚼		
28	⚺	∠			⚼		△	△	✱
29		⚺			△	☍			∠
30			✱	✱				□	
31	☌		∠	∠	□		□		⚺

D M	Saturn Lat.	Saturn Dec.	Uranus Lat.	Uranus Dec.	Neptune Lat.	Neptune Dec.	Pluto Lat.	Pluto Dec.
	° ′	° ′	° ′	° ′	° ′	° ′	° ′	° ′
1	2S45	4N21	0S38	19S41	0N24	20S20	12N 7	8S56
3	2 46	4 18	0 38	19 41	0 24	20 20	12 6	8 58
5	2 46	4 14	0 38	19 41	0 24	20 20	12 6	8 59
7	2 46	4 10	0 38	19 41	0 24	20 20	12 5	9 0
9	2 46	4 7	0 38	19 41	0 24	20 20	12 4	9 2
11	2 46	4 3	0 38	19 41	0 23	20 20	12 3	9 3
13	2 46	3 59	0 38	19 41	0 23	20 20	12 3	9 4
15	2 46	3 56	0 38	19 41	0 23	20 20	12 2	9 6
17	2 46	3 52	0 38	19 41	0 23	20 20	12 1	9 7
19	2 46	3 49	0 38	19 41	0 23	20 20	12 0	9 8
21	2 45	3 45	0 38	19 41	0 23	20 20	12 0	9 10
23	2 45	3 42	0 38	19 41	0 23	20 20	11 59	9 11
25	2 45	3 39	0 37	19 40	0 23	20 20	11 59	9 12
27	2 45	3 36	0 37	19 40	0 23	20 20	11 58	9 13
29	2 45	3 33	0 37	19 40	0 23	20 19	11 58	9 15
31	2S44	3N29	0S37	19S39	0N23	20S19	11N57	9S16

Mutual Aspects

1 ♀Q♅. ♀P♆.
2 ♀±♄. ♂⚼♄.
3 ♂☌♇.
4 ☿✱♂. ☿△♅. ☿✱♇. ☉P♄.
5 ☉△♃. ♀✱♆. ♂✱♅.
8 ♀Q♃. ♀P♂. ♃Stat.
9 ☉∠♀. ☿△♃. ☿P♄. ♆Stat.
10 ☉☍♄. ♀⚼♄.
11 ☿☍♄. ♀☌♇.
12 ☉∠♇. ☿∠♇. ♀✱♅. ♄Q♅.
13 ☉☌☿.
14 ☿∠♀. ♅Stat.
16 ♂✱♃. ♂∠♆. ☉P☿. ☉P♇. ☿P♇.
17 ☿□♆. 18 ☿⊥♇.
19 ☿∠♂. ♀✱♃. ♀∠♆.
20 ☉□♆.
21 ☉⊥♇. ♂△♄.
22 ☿□♅. ☿⚺♇. ♀△♄.
26 ♀☌♂. ♀∠♅. ♂∠♅.
27 ☉⚺♇. ☿□♃. ♀⊥♆.
28 ☉□♅. ♂⊥♆.
29 ☿⊥♂. ☿∇♄. ☿Q♆.
30 ☿P♃. 31 ☿⊥♀.

LAST QUARTER-Oct.23, 4h.48m. am. (29°♋49′)

NEW MOON-Nov.30, 2h.14m. am. (7°♐ 54′)

D M	D W	Sidereal Time	☉ Long.	☉ Dec.	☽ Long.	☽ Lat.	☽ Dec.	☽ Node	Midnight ☽ Long.	Midnight ☽ Dec.
		H. M. S.	° ′ ″	° ′	° ′ ″	° ′	° ′	° ′	° ′ ″	° ′
1	S	14 43 15	9 ♏ 6 2	14 S 32	21 ♏ 24 29	4 N33	13 S 43	16 ♍ 56	27 ♏ 40 8	14 S 59
2	Su	14 47 12	10 6 7	14 51	3 ♐ 58 45	4 57	16 5	16 53	10 ♐ 20 21	17 0
3	M	14 51 8	11 6 13	15 9	16 44 57	5 6	17 42	16 49	23 12 35	18 11
4	T	14 55 5	12 6 21	15 28	29 43 17	5 0	18 26	16 46	6 ♑ 17 6	18 27
5	W	14 59 1	13 6 31	15 46	12 ♑ 54 6	4 38	18 12	16 43	19 34 22	17 42
6	Th	15 2 58	14 6 42	16 4	26 18 1	4 1	16 57	16 40	3 ♒ 5 8	15 57
7	F	15 6 55	15 6 55	16 22	9 ♒ 55 50	3 9	14 43	16 37	16 50 14	13 16
8	S	15 10 51	16 7 9	16 40	23 48 22	2 6	11 36	16 34	0 ♓ 50 17	9 46
9	Su	15 14 48	17 7 24	16 57	7 ♓ 55 57	0 N53	7 46	16 30	15 5 13	5 38
10	M	15 18 44	18 7 41	17 14	22 17 52	0 S23	3 S25	16 27	29 33 34	1 S 7
11	T	15 22 41	19 8 0	17 30	6 ♈ 51 51	1 39	1 N12	16 24	14 ♈ 12 7	3 N31
12	W	15 26 37	20 8 19	17 47	21 33 39	2 49	5 47	16 21	28 55 37	7 58
13	Th	15 30 34	21 8 41	18 3	6 ♉ 17 8	3 48	10 1	16 18	13 ♉ 37 13	11 55
14	F	15 34 30	22 9 4	18 18	20 54 54	4 31	13 37	16 15	28 9 15	15 6
15	S	15 38 27	23 9 28	18 34	5 ♊ 19 22	4 56	16 19	16 11	12 ♊ 24 32	17 17
16	Su	15 42 24	24 9 55	18 49	19 24 4	5 3	17 59	16 8	26 17 32	18 24
17	M	15 46 20	25 10 23	19 3	3 ♋ 4 37	4 52	18 33	16 5	9 ♋ 45 10	18 26
18	T	15 50 17	26 10 53	19 18	16 19 13	4 25	18 4	16 2	22 46 56	17 28
19	W	15 54 13	27 11 24	19 32	29 8 36	3 45	16 39	15 59	5 ♌ 24 39	15 39
20	Th	15 58 10	28 11 57	19 45	11 ♌ 35 35	2 56	14 29	15 55	17 41 59	13 10
21	F	16 2 6	29 ♏ 12 32	19 59	23 44 29	1 59	11 44	15 52	29 43 45	10 10
22	S	16 6 3	0 ♐ 13 9	20 12	5 ♍ 40 29	0 S59	8 31	15 49	11 ♍ 35 24	6 48
23	Su	16 9 59	1 13 48	20 24	17 29 10	0 N 4	5 0	15 46	23 22 30	3 N10
24	M	16 13 56	2 14 28	20 36	29 16 4	1 6	1 N18	15 43	5 ♎ 10 29	0 S35
25	T	16 17 53	3 15 9	20 48	11 ♎ 6 21	2 5	2 S28	15 40	17 4 12	4 20
26	W	16 21 49	4 15 52	21 0	23 4 31	3 0	6 11	15 36	29 7 45	7 58
27	Th	16 25 46	5 16 37	21 11	5 ♏ 14 13	3 47	9 42	15 33	11 ♏ 24 12	11 20
28	F	16 29 42	6 17 23	21 21	17 37 55	4 24	12 52	15 30	23 55 27	14 15
29	S	16 33 39	7 18 11	21 32	0 ♐ 16 52	4 49	15 30	15 27	6 ♐ 42 7	16 33
30	Su	16 37 35	8 ♐ 19 0	21 S 41	13 ♐ 11 7	5 N 0	17 S 25	15 ♍ 24	19 ♐ 43 41	18 S 4

D M	Mercury Lat.	Mercury Dec.		Venus Lat.	Venus Dec.		Mars Lat.	Mars Dec.		Jupiter Lat.	Jupiter Dec.
	° ′	° ′	° ′	° ′	° ′	° ′	° ′	° ′	° ′	° ′	° ′
1	1 S 5	18 S 57	19 S 27	3 S 29	26 S 51	26 S 55	1 S 14	24 S 32	24 S 34	0 S 56	17 S 48
3	1 17	19 56	20 24	3 32	26 57	26 59	1 14	24 36	24 37	0 56	17 45
5	1 29	20 51	21 17	3 34	27 0	27 0	1 14	24 39	24 40	0 56	17 41
7	1 40	21 42	22 6	3 35	27 0	27 0	1 14	24 40	24 41	0 56	17 38
9	1 51	22 29	22 51	3 36	26 59	26 57	1 15	24 41	24 41	0 55	17 35
11	2 0	23 12	23 31	3 37	26 54	26 51	1 15	24 40	24 40	0 55	17 31
13	2 9	23 50	24 7	3 36	26 48	26 43	1 15	24 39	24 38	0 55	17 27
15	2 17	24 23	24 38	3 35	26 39	26 34	1 15	24 36	24 35	0 55	17 23
17	2 23	24 51	25 3	3 33	26 28	26 21	1 15	24 33	24 30	0 55	17 18
19	2 27	25 14	25 23	3 31	26 15	26 7	1 15	24 28	24 25	0 55	17 14
21	2 30	25 31	25 38	3 27	26 0	25 51	1 16	24 22	24 19	0 54	17 9
23	2 31	25 43	25 47	3 23	25 43	25 33	1 16	24 15	24 11	0 54	17 4
25	2 30	25 49	25 50	3 17	25 24	25 14	1 16	24 7	24 3	0 54	16 59
27	2 26	25 49	25 47	3 11	25 3	24 53	1 15	23 58	23 53	0 54	16 53
29	2 18	25 44	25 S 39	3 4	24 41	24 S 30	1 15	23 48	23 S 42	0 54	16 48
31	2 S 7	25 S 33		2 S 55	24 S 18		1 S 15	23 S 36		0 S 54	16 S 42

FIRST QUARTER-Nov. 7, 9h.43m. pm. (15°♒31′)

FULL MOON-Nov.14, 2h.12m. pm. (22° ♉ 15′)

D M	☿ Long.	♀ Long.	♂ Long.	♃ Long.	♄ Long.	♅ Long.	♆ Long.	♇ Long.	☉	☿	♀	♂	♃	♄	♅	♆	♇
	° ′	° ′	° ′	° ′	° ′	° ′	° ′	° ′	Lunar Aspects								
1	20♏36	26♐ 3	24♐13	13♒ 3	15♈13	4♒53	27♑20	4♐28		☌	⚺	⚺				✱	
2	22 7	27 5	24 58	13 8	15R 9	4 53	27 21	4 30						⚼	✱		☌
3	23 38	28 6	25 43	13 13	15 5	4 54	27 22	4 32	⚺				✱	△	∠	∠	
4	25 9	29♐ 7	26 27	13 18	15 1	4 55	27 22	4 34	∠	⚺	☌	☌	∠		⚺	⚺	⚺
5	26 40	0♑ 8	27 12	13 24	14 57	4 57	27 23	4 37	✱	∠			⚺	□			
6	28 9	1 8	27 57	13 29	14 54	4 58	27 24	4 39		✱	⚺	⚺				☌	∠
7	29♏39	2 8	28 42	13 35	14 50	4 59	27 25	4 41	□			∠	☌	✱	☌		✱
8	1♐ 8	3 8	29♐27	13 40	14 46	5 0	27 26	4 43			∠	✱		∠		⚺	
9	2 36	4 7	0♑12	13 46	14 43	5 1	27 27	4 46		□	✱		⚺	⚺	⚺	∠	□
10	4 4	5 5	0 57	13 53	14 39	5 3	27 28	4 48	△				∠		∠	✱	
11	5 32	6 3	1 42	13 59	14 36	5 4	27 29	4 50	⚼	△	□	□	✱		✱		△
12	6 59	7 1	2 28	14 5	14 32	5 6	27 31	4 53		⚼				●		□	⚼
13	8 25	7 58	3 13	14 12	14 29	5 7	27 32	4 55			△	△			□		
14	9 51	8 55	3 58	14 19	14 26	5 9	27 33	4 57	☍		⚼	⚼	□	⚺		△	
15	11 16	9 51	4 44	14 26	14 22	5 10	27 34	5 0		☍				∠	△		☍
16	12 40	10 47	5 29	14 33	14 19	5 12	27 35	5 2					△	✱	⚼	⚼	
17	14 4	11 42	6 15	14 40	14 16	5 14	27 37	5 4				☍	⚼				
18	15 27	12 36	7 0	14 48	14 13	5 15	27 38	5 7	⚼		☍			□			⚼
19	16 48	13 30	7 46	14 55	14 11	5 17	27 39	5 9	△	⚼					☍	☍	△
20	18 9	14 23	8 32	15 3	14 8	5 19	27 40	5 11					☍	△			
21	19 28	15 16	9 18	15 11	14 5	5 21	27 42	5 14	□	△		⚼		⚼			
22	20 46	16 8	10 3	15 19	14 3	5 23	27 43	5 16			⚼	△					□
23	22 2	16 59	10 49	15 27	14 0	5 24	27 45	5 18		□	△				⚼	⚼	
24	23 16	17 49	11 35	15 36	13 58	5 26	27 46	5 21	✱				⚼			△	
25	24 28	18 39	12 21	15 44	13 56	5 28	27 48	5 23				□	△	☍	△		✱
26	25 38	19 28	13 7	15 53	13 54	5 31	27 49	5 25	∠	✱	□					□	∠
27	26 45	20 16	13 53	16 1	13 51	5 33	27 51	5 28	⚺						□		⚺
28	27 48	21 3	14 39	16 10	13 49	5 35	27 52	5 30		∠	✱	✱	□				
29	28 48	21 50	15 26	16 19	13 48	5 37	27 54	5 32		⚺		∠		⚼	✱	✱	☌
30	29♐44	22♑35	16♑12	16♒28	13♈46	5♒39	27♑55	5♐35	☌		∠	⚺	✱	△		∠	

D M	Saturn Lat.	Saturn Dec.	Uranus Lat.	Uranus Dec.	Neptune Lat.	Neptune Dec.	Pluto Lat.	Pluto Dec.
	° ′	° ′	° ′	° ′	° ′	° ′	° ′	° ′
1	2S44	3N28	0S37	19S39	0N23	20S19	11N57	9S17
3	2 44	3 25	0 37	19 38	0 23	20 19	11 56	9 18
5	2 44	3 22	0 37	19 38	0 23	20 18	11 56	9 19
7	2 44	3 20	0 37	19 37	0 23	20 18	11 55	9 20
9	2 43	3 17	0 37	19 37	0 23	20 18	11 55	9 21
11	2 43	3 15	0 37	19 36	0 23	20 17	11 55	9 22
13	2 43	3 13	0 37	19 35	0 23	20 17	11 54	9 24
15	2 42	3 10	0 37	19 34	0 23	20 17	11 54	9 25
17	2 42	3 8	0 37	19 33	0 23	20 16	11 54	9 26
19	2 41	3 7	0 37	19 32	0 23	20 16	11 53	9 27
21	2 41	3 5	0 37	19 32	0 23	20 15	11 53	9 28
23	2 40	3 3	0 37	19 31	0 22	20 15	11 53	9 29
25	2 40	3 2	0 37	19 30	0 22	20 14	11 53	9 30
27	2 40	3 1	0 37	19 28	0 22	20 13	11 53	9 31
29	2 39	3 0	0 37	19 27	0 22	20 13	11 52	9 32
31	2S39	2N59	0S37	19S26	0N22	20S12	11N52	9S33

Mutual Aspects

1 ☉∠♂. ☿±♄.
2 ♀⚺♆. ☿P♅.
3 ☿Q♅. ♀∠♃.
4 ♀⊥♅. ☿P♆.
5 ☉□♃. ☿✱♆. ♂⚺♆.
6 ☿⚺♂.
7 ☉∇♄. ☉Q♆. ☿⚼♄. ♂∠♃. ♂⊥♅.
8 ☿Q♃.
10 ♀⚺♅. ♀⚺♇.
11 ☿✱♅. ☿☌♇. ☉P♃.
12 ☉±♄. ☿⚺♀.
13 ♀⊥♃.
15 ☉Q♅. ♂⚺♇. ♃✱♄.
16 ☿∠♆. ♀⊥♇. ♂⚺♅. ☿P♂.
17 ☿✱♃. ☿△♄.
19 ☉✱♆. ☉P♅.
20 ♀□♄.
21 ☉⚼♄. ♀⚺♃. ♂⊥♃.
22 ☿∠♅. ☉P♆.
23 ☿⊥♆. ☿P♀.
24 ♂⊥♇. 26 ☉Q♃.
27 ☉∠♀. ☉✱♅. ☉☌♇. ♀∠♇. ♂□♄.
28 ☿⚺♆.
30 ☿⊥♅. ♂⚺♃.

LAST QUARTER-Nov.21,11h.58m. pm. (29° ♌ 43′)

NEW MOON-Dec.29, 4h.57m. pm. (8°♑ 1′)

D M	D W	Sidereal Time	☉ Long.	☉ Dec.	☽ Long.	☽ Lat.	☽ Dec.	☽ Node	Midnight ☽ Long.	Midnight ☽ Dec.
		H. M. S.	° ′ ″	° ′	° ′ ″	° ′	° ′	° ′	° ′ ″	° ′
1	M	16 41 32	9 ♐ 19 50	21 S 51	26 ♐ 19 37	4 N55	18 S 28	15 ♍ 21	2 ♑ 58 41	18 S 38
2	T	16 45 28	10 20 41	22 0	9 ♑ 40 38	4 34	18 31	15 17	16 25 13	18 10
3	W	16 49 25	11 21 34	22 8	23 12 11	3 58	17 32	15 14	0 ♒ 1 20	16 39
4	Th	16 53 22	12 22 27	22 17	6 ♒ 52 28	3 7	15 32	15 11	13 45 28	14 11
5	F	16 57 18	13 23 21	22 24	20 40 12	2 5	12 37	15 8	27 36 39	10 52
6	S	17 1 15	14 24 15	22 32	4 ♓ 34 44	0 N55	8 58	15 5	11 ♓ 34 26	6 56
7	Su	17 5 11	15 25 11	22 38	18 35 45	0 S18	4 48	15 1	25 38 37	2 S35
8	M	17 9 8	16 26 7	22 45	2 ♈ 42 57	1 32	0 S19	14 58	9 ♈ 48 39	1 N57
9	T	17 13 4	17 27 3	22 51	16 55 30	2 40	4 N11	14 55	24 3 13	6 23
10	W	17 17 1	18 28 1	22 56	1 ♉ 11 27	3 38	8 29	14 52	8 ♉ 19 45	10 27
11	Th	17 20 57	19 28 59	23 1	15 27 35	4 22	12 17	14 49	22 34 22	13 55
12	F	17 24 54	20 29 57	23 6	29 39 26	4 50	15 21	14 46	6 ♊ 42 8	16 32
13	S	17 28 51	21 30 57	23 10	13 ♊ 41 49	5 0	17 28	14 42	20 37 51	18 8
14	Su	17 32 47	22 31 57	23 14	27 29 42	4 53	18 32	14 39	4 ♋ 16 51	18 40
15	M	17 36 44	23 32 58	23 17	10 ♋ 58 59	4 28	18 31	14 36	17 35 49	18 8
16	T	17 40 40	24 33 59	23 20	24 7 15	3 50	17 30	14 33	0 ♌ 33 17	16 39
17	W	17 44 37	25 35 2	23 22	6 ♌ 54 3	3 2	15 37	14 30	13 9 47	14 24
18	Th	17 48 33	26 36 5	23 24	19 20 50	2 5	13 2	14 27	25 27 37	11 33
19	F	17 52 30	27 37 9	23 25	1 ♍ 30 40	1 4	9 56	14 23	7 ♍ 30 33	8 15
20	S	17 56 26	28 38 14	23 26	13 27 53	0 S 1	6 29	14 20	19 23 20	4 40
21	Su	18 0 23	29 ♐ 39 20	23 26	25 17 35	1 N 2	2 N49	14 17	1 ♎ 11 20	0 N56
22	M	18 4 20	0 ♑ 40 26	23 26	7 ♎ 5 18	2 1	0 S57	14 14	13 0 10	2 S50
23	T	18 8 16	1 41 34	23 26	18 56 37	2 56	4 42	14 11	24 55 17	6 32
24	W	18 12 13	2 42 41	23 25	0 ♏ 56 49	3 44	8 18	14 7	7 ♏ 1 45	10 0
25	Th	18 16 9	3 43 50	23 23	13 10 35	4 22	11 37	14 4	19 23 45	13 8
26	F	18 20 6	4 44 59	23 21	25 41 34	4 49	14 30	14 1	2 ♐ 4 17	15 43
27	S	18 24 2	5 46 9	23 19	8 ♐ 32 2	5 2	16 45	13 58	15 4 51	17 35
28	Su	18 27 59	6 47 19	23 16	21 42 38	4 59	18 12	13 55	28 25 11	18 34
29	M	18 31 55	7 48 29	23 12	5 ♑ 12 13	4 40	18 40	13 52	12 ♑ 3 21	18 30
30	T	18 35 52	8 49 40	23 9	18 58 6	4 4	18 4	13 48	25 55 58	17 20
31	W	18 39 49	9 ♑ 50 50	23 S 4	2 ♒ 56 25	3 N14	16 S21	13 ♍ 45	9 ♒ 58 53	15 S 7

D M	Mercury Lat.	Mercury Dec.	Mercury Dec.	Venus Lat.	Venus Dec.	Venus Dec.	Mars Lat.	Mars Dec.	Mars Dec.	Jupiter Lat.	Jupiter Dec.
	° ′	° ′	° ′	° ′	° ′	° ′	° ′	° ′	° ′	° ′	° ′
1	2 S 7	25 S 33	25 S 26	2 S 55	24 S 18	24 S 6	1 S 15	23 S 36	23 S 30	0 S 54	16 S 42
3	1 52	25 17	25 7	2 46	23 53	23 41	1 15	23 24	23 17	0 54	16 36
5	1 31	24 55	24 43	2 35	23 28	23 15	1 15	23 11	23 3	0 53	16 30
7	1 5	24 29	24 14	2 23	23 1	22 47	1 15	22 56	22 48	0 53	16 24
9	0 S 34	23 58	23 41	2 10	22 34	22 20	1 15	22 41	22 32	0 53	16 18
11	0 N 2	23 23	23 4	1 55	22 6	21 51	1 14	22 24	22 15	0 53	16 11
13	0 42	22 44	22 24	1 39	21 37	21 23	1 14	22 6	21 57	0 53	16 4
15	1 22	22 3	21 43	1 21	21 8	20 54	1 14	21 48	21 38	0 53	15 58
17	1 59	21 22	21 3	1 2	20 40	20 25	1 13	21 28	21 18	0 53	15 51
19	2 28	20 45	20 29	0 41	20 11	19 57	1 13	21 8	20 57	0 53	15 43
21	2 49	20 16	20 5	0 S 19	19 42	19 28	1 13	20 46	20 35	0 53	15 36
23	3 0	19 57	19 51	0 N 5	19 14	19 0	1 12	20 24	20 13	0 52	15 29
25	3 3	19 49	19 49	0 31	18 47	18 33	1 12	20 1	19 49	0 52	15 21
27	2 58	19 51	19 56	0 58	18 20	18 7	1 11	19 37	19 24	0 52	15 13
29	2 49	20 2	20 S 10	1 26	17 55	17 S 42	1 11	19 12	18 S 59	0 52	15 5
31	2 N36	20 S 19		1 N 55	17 S 30		1 S 10	18 S 46		0 S 52	14 S 57

FIRST QUARTER-Dec. 7, 6h. 9m. am. (15°♓10′)

FULL MOON-Dec.14, 2h.37m. am. (22°♊ 8′)

D	☿	♀	♂	♃	♄	♅	♆	♇	Lunar Aspects								
M	Long.	Long.	Long.	Long.	Long.	Long.	Long.	Long.	☉	☿	♀	♂	♃	♄	♅	♆	♇
	° ′	° ′	° ′	° ′	° ′	° ′	° ′	° ′									
1	0♑35	23♑19	16♑58	16♒38	13♈44	5♒42	27♑57	5♐37		☌	⚺		∠		∠	⚺	
2	1 21	24 3	17 44	16 47	13R 43	5 44	27 59	5 40	⚺					□	⚺		⚺
3	2 1	24 45	18 31	16 57	13 41	5 46	28 0	5 42	∠		☌	☌	⚺			☌	∠
4	2 33	25 26	19 17	17 6	13 40	5 49	28 2	5 44	⚹	⚺				⚹	☌		⚹
5	2 58	26 6	20 4	17 16	13 39	5 51	28 4	5 47		∠	⚺	⚺	☌				
6	3 15	26 45	20 50	17 26	13 37	5 53	28 6	5 49		⚹		∠		∠	⚺	⚺	□
7	3 22	27 22	21 37	17 36	13 36	5 56	28 7	5 51	□		∠	⚹	⚺	⚺	∠	∠	
8	3R 19	27 59	22 23	17 46	13 36	5 59	28 9	5 54		□	⚹		∠		⚹	⚹	△
9	3 5	28 34	23 10	17 57	13 35	6 1	28 11	5 56	△			□	⚹	●			⚼
10	2 40	29 7	23 56	18 7	13 34	6 4	28 13	5 58	⚼	△	□				□	□	
11	2 3	29♑39	24 43	18 17	13 33	6 6	28 15	6 1		⚼			□	⚺			
12	1 15	0♒ 9	25 30	18 28	13 33	6 9	28 17	6 3			△	△		∠	△	△	☍
13	0♑16	0 38	26 16	18 39	13 33	6 12	28 18	6 5			⚼	⚼	△	⚹		⚼	
14	29♐ 9	1 5	27 3	18 50	13 32	6 14	28 20	6 8	☍	☍			⚼		⚼		
15	27 53	1 30	27 50	19 1	13 32	6 17	28 22	6 10						□			
16	26 33	1 54	28 37	19 12	13D 32	6 20	28 24	6 12				☍				☍	⚼
17	25 10	2 15	29♑24	19 23	13 32	6 23	28 26	6 14	⚼	⚼	☍				☍		△
18	23 48	2 35	0♒11	19 34	13 32	6 26	28 28	6 17		△			☍	△			
19	22 28	2 53	0 57	19 45	13 33	6 29	28 30	6 19	△					⚼			□
20	21 15	3 8	1 44	19 57	13 33	6 32	28 32	6 21			⚼	⚼				⚼	
21	20 8	3 22	2 31	20 8	13 33	6 35	28 34	6 23	□	□					⚼	△	
22	19 11	3 33	3 18	20 20	13 34	6 38	28 36	6 26			△	△	⚼		△		⚹
23	18 25	3 43	4 5	20 32	13 35	6 41	28 38	6 28		⚹			△	☍			∠
24	17 48	3 49	4 52	20 43	13 36	6 44	28 41	6 30	⚹	∠	□	□			□	□	⚺
25	17 23	3 54	5 39	20 55	13 37	6 47	28 43	6 32	∠	⚺							
26	17 8	3 56	6 27	21 7	13 38	6 50	28 45	6 34					□	⚼		⚹	
27	17D 4	3R 56	7 14	21 19	13 39	6 53	28 47	6 36	⚺		⚹	⚹		△	⚹	∠	☌
28	17 8	3 53	8 1	21 32	13 40	6 56	28 49	6 38		☌	∠	∠	⚹		∠		
29	17 22	3 48	8 48	21 44	13 41	6 59	28 51	6 41	☌		⚺	⚺	∠		⚺	⚺	⚺
30	17 43	3 40	9 35	21 56	13 43	7 2	28 53	6 43		⚺			⚺	□			∠
31	18♐12	3♒30	10♒22	22♒ 9	13♈45	7♒ 6	28♑56	6♐45		∠	☌				☌	☌	⚹

D	Saturn		Uranus		Neptune		Pluto	
M	Lat.	Dec.	Lat.	Dec.	Lat.	Dec.	Lat.	Dec.
	° ′	° ′	° ′	° ′	° ′	° ′	° ′	° ′
1	2S39	2N59	0S37	19S26	0N22	20S12	11N52	9S33
3	2 38	2 58	0 37	19 25	0 22	20 12	11 52	9 33
5	2 38	2 58	0 36	19 24	0 22	20 11	11 52	9 34
7	2 37	2 57	0 36	19 23	0 22	20 10	11 52	9 35
9	2 37	2 57	0 36	19 21	0 22	20 10	11 52	9 36
11	2 36	2 57	0 36	19 20	0 22	20 9	11 52	9 37
13	2 36	2 57	0 36	19 19	0 22	20 8	11 52	9 37
15	2 35	2 58	0 36	19 17	0 22	20 7	11 52	9 38
17	2 34	2 58	0 36	19 16	0 22	20 7	11 52	9 39
19	2 34	2 59	0 36	19 14	0 22	20 6	11 52	9 39
21	2 33	3 0	0 36	19 13	0 22	20 5	11 53	9 40
23	2 33	3 1	0 36	19 11	0 22	20 4	11 53	9 40
25	2 32	3 2	0 36	19 10	0 22	20 4	11 53	9 41
27	2 32	3 3	0 36	19 8	0 22	20 3	11 53	9 41
29	2 31	3 5	0 36	19 6	0 22	20 2	11 53	9 42
31	2S31	3N 6	0S36	19S 5	0N22	20S 1	11N54	9S42

Mutual Aspects

3 ☿∠♃.
5 ☉△♄. ☉∠♆.
6 ♂∠♇. 7 ☿Stat.
8 ☉⊥♂. ♀☌♆. ☉P♀. ☉P♂. ♀P♂.
9 ☿∠♃. ♃Q♇.
10 ☉⚹♃. 12 ☉P☿.
13 ☉∠♅. ☿⚺♀. ☿⊥♅.
14 ☉⊥♆.
15 ☿⚺♂. ☿⚺♆. ♀Q♄.
16 ☿⊥♀. ♂☌♆. ☿P♂. ♄Stat.
17 ☉☌☿.
18 ☉⊥♀. ☿⊥♂.
19 ☿⊥♆. ♀P♆.
20 ☉⚺♆. ☿∠♅. ♂Q♄.
21 ☿⚹♃.
22 ☉⊥♅. ♀☌♂. ☿P♆.
23 ☿∠♀ ☿∠♂. ♀P♅.
25 ☉⚺♀. ♂P♆.
26 ♂⚹♇. ☿P♂. ♀Stat.
27 ♂☌♅. ☿Stat.
28 ☉∠♃. ☉⚺♅. ☉⚺♇.
29 ☿P♆. ♂P♅.
31 ☿∠♀.

LAST QUARTER-Dec.21, 9h.43m. pm. (0°♎ 4′)

JANUARY

D	☉	☽	☽Dec.	☿	♀	♂
	° ′ ″	° ′ ″	° ′	° ′	° ′	′
1	1 01 10	12 11 48	3 47	1 21	1 15	20
2	1 01 10	12 30 46	3 39	1 21	1 15	19
3	1 01 10	12 54 45	3 20	1 18	1 15	19
4	1 01 10	13 22 33	2 48	1 12	1 15	18
5	1 01 11	13 52 07	2 02	1 05	1 15	18
6	1 01 11	14 20 32	1 02	0 56	1 15	18
7	1 01 11	14 44 28	0 09	0 47	1 15	17
8	1 01 11	15 00 41	1 25	0 37	1 15	17
9	1 01 10	15 07 04	2 35	0 27	1 15	16
10	1 01 10	15 03 14	3 31	0 17	1 15	16
11	1 01 09	14 50 34	4 10	0 08	1 15	15
12	1 01 09	14 31 43	4 28	0 01	1 15	15
13	1 01 08	14 09 40	4 28	0 09	1 15	14
14	1 01 07	13 47 05	4 13	0 17	1 15	14
15	1 01 07	13 25 50	3 46	0 24	1 15	13
16	1 01 06	13 06 59	3 09	0 30	1 15	13
17	1 01 05	12 50 52	2 25	0 36	1 15	12
18	1 01 04	12 37 22	1 36	0 41	1 15	12
19	1 01 03	12 26 04	0 44	0 46	1 15	11
20	1 01 03	12 16 30	0 08	0 50	1 15	11
21	1 01 02	12 08 17	0 58	0 53	1 15	10
22	1 01 01	12 01 11	1 44	0 57	1 15	9
23	1 01 00	11 55 15	2 23	1 00	1 15	9
24	1 00 59	11 50 45	2 54	1 03	1 15	8
25	1 00 59	11 48 11	3 18	1 05	1 15	8
26	1 00 58	11 48 12	3 35	1 08	1 15	7
27	1 00 57	11 51 30	3 43	1 10	1 15	6
28	1 00 56	11 58 48	3 44	1 12	1 15	6
29	1 00 56	12 10 40	3 38	1 13	1 15	5
30	1 00 55	12 27 28	3 22	1 15	1 15	4
31	1 00 54	12 49 10	2 56	1 17	1 15	4

FEBRUARY

D	☉	☽	☽Dec.	☿	♀	♂
	° ′ ″	° ′ ″	° ′	° ′	° ′	′
1	1 00 54	13 15 09	2 19	1 18	1 15	3
2	1 00 53	13 44 02	1 28	1 19	1 15	2
3	1 00 52	14 13 34	0 25	1 21	1 15	1
4	1 00 51	14 40 42	0 46	1 22	1 15	1
5	1 00 50	15 02 00	1 59	1 23	1 15	0
6	1 00 49	15 14 27	3 05	1 24	1 15	1
7	1 00 48	15 16 19	3 57	1 25	1 15	1
8	1 00 46	15 07 39	4 28	1 26	1 15	2
9	1 00 45	14 50 15	4 38	1 27	1 15	3
10	1 00 43	14 26 56	4 29	1 28	1 15	4
11	1 00 41	14 00 51	4 03	1 29	1 15	5
12	1 00 40	13 34 40	3 26	1 30	1 15	5
13	1 00 38	13 10 20	2 41	1 31	1 15	6
14	1 00 36	12 49 02	1 51	1 32	1 15	7
15	1 00 35	12 31 18	0 58	1 33	1 15	8
16	1 00 33	12 17 09	0 06	1 34	1 15	8
17	1 00 31	12 06 22	0 44	1 34	1 15	9
18	1 00 29	11 58 33	1 30	1 35	1 15	10
19	1 00 28	11 53 15	2 11	1 36	1 15	11
20	1 00 26	11 50 10	2 44	1 37	1 15	12
21	1 00 24	11 49 03	3 11	1 38	1 15	12
22	1 00 23	11 49 51	3 30	1 39	1 15	13
23	1 00 21	11 52 42	3 41	1 40	1 15	14
24	1 00 19	11 57 52	3 44	1 41	1 15	15
25	1 00 18	12 05 44	3 39	1 42	1 15	15
26	1 00 16	12 16 41	3 25	1 43	1 15	16
27	1 00 15	12 31 05	3 01	1 44	1 15	17
28	1 00 13	12 49 05	2 27	1 45	1 15	17

MARCH

D	☉	☽	☽Dec.	☿	♀	♂
	° ′ ″	° ′ ″	° ′	° ′	° ′	′
1	1 00 12	13 10 30	1 43	1 46	1 15	18
2	1 00 10	13 34 39	0 47	1 47	1 15	19
3	1 00 09	14 00 10	0 16	1 48	1 15	19
4	1 00 07	14 25 02	1 25	1 49	1 15	20
5	1 00 06	14 46 41	2 32	1 50	1 15	20
6	1 00 04	15 02 22	3 30	1 51	1 15	21
7	1 00 02	15 09 49	4 13	1 53	1 15	21
8	1 00 00	15 07 46	4 37	1 54	1 15	22
9	0 59 58	14 56 28	4 39	1 55	1 15	22
10	0 59 56	14 37 26	4 22	1 56	1 15	22
11	0 59 54	14 13 09	3 49	1 56	1 15	23
12	0 59 52	13 46 23	3 04	1 57	1 15	23
13	0 59 50	13 19 37	2 11	1 58	1 15	23
14	0 59 48	12 54 52	1 16	1 59	1 15	23
15	0 59 45	12 33 26	0 21	1 59	1 15	23
16	0 59 43	12 16 03	0 31	2 00	1 15	23
17	0 59 41	12 03 01	1 18	2 00	1 15	24
18	0 59 39	11 54 14	2 00	2 00	1 15	24
19	0 59 36	11 49 25	2 35	1 59	1 15	23
20	0 59 34	11 48 08	3 04	1 59	1 15	23
21	0 59 32	11 49 54	3 25	1 58	1 15	23
22	0 59 30	11 54 15	3 39	1 56	1 15	23
23	0 59 28	12 00 48	3 45	1 55	1 15	23
24	0 59 26	12 09 14	3 42	1 53	1 15	23
25	0 59 24	12 19 19	3 30	1 50	1 15	22
26	0 59 22	12 30 59	3 08	1 47	1 15	22
27	0 59 20	12 44 13	2 36	1 44	1 15	22
28	0 59 18	12 59 02	1 53	1 40	1 15	21
29	0 59 17	13 15 22	1 01	1 36	1 15	21
30	0 59 15	13 33 00	0 02	1 32	1 15	20
31	0 59 13	13 51 22	1 02	1 27	1 15	20

APRIL

D	☉	☽	☽Dec.	☿	♀	♂
	° ′ ″	° ′ ″	° ′	° ′	° ′	′
1	0 59 11	14 09 35	2 05	1 22	1 14	19
2	0 59 10	14 26 17	3 03	1 16	1 14	19
3	0 59 08	14 39 47	3 51	1 10	1 14	18
4	0 59 06	14 48 19	4 23	1 04	1 14	17
5	0 59 04	14 50 22	4 37	0 58	1 14	17
6	0 59 02	14 45 03	4 32	0 52	1 14	16
7	0 59 00	14 32 27	4 08	0 46	1 14	15
8	0 58 58	14 13 40	3 29	0 39	1 14	15
9	0 58 56	13 50 36	2 38	0 33	1 14	14
10	0 58 54	13 25 31	1 41	0 26	1 14	13
11	0 58 51	13 00 39	0 42	0 19	1 14	12
12	0 58 49	12 37 55	0 14	0 13	1 14	12
13	0 58 47	12 18 42	1 05	0 06	1 14	11
14	0 58 45	12 03 53	1 49	0 00	1 14	10
15	0 58 42	11 53 55	2 26	0 06	1 14	9
16	0 58 40	11 48 52	2 57	0 12	1 14	8
17	0 58 38	11 48 30	3 20	0 17	1 14	8
18	0 58 36	11 52 25	3 36	0 22	1 14	7
19	0 58 34	11 59 59	3 45	0 27	1 14	6
20	0 58 32	12 10 28	3 46	0 31	1 14	5
21	0 58 30	12 23 03	3 38	0 34	1 14	4
22	0 58 28	12 36 54	3 19	0 37	1 14	4
23	0 58 26	12 51 12	2 49	0 39	1 14	3
24	0 58 24	13 05 17	2 08	0 40	1 14	2
25	0 58 23	13 18 41	1 16	0 41	1 14	1
26	0 58 21	13 31 10	0 17	0 40	1 14	1
27	0 58 19	13 42 41	0 46	0 39	1 14	0
28	0 58 18	13 53 18	1 49	0 38	1 14	1
29	0 58 16	14 03 02	2 46	0 35	1 14	2
30	0 58 15	14 11 41	3 33	0 33	1 14	2

MAY

D	☉	☽	☽Dec.	☿	♀	♂
	° ′ ″	° ′ ″	° ′	° ′	° ′	′
1	0 58 13	14 18 46	4 08	0 29	1 14	3
2	0 58 12	14 23 28	4 28	0 26	1 14	4
3	0 58 10	14 24 44	4 31	0 22	1 14	4
4	0 58 09	14 21 34	4 17	0 17	1 14	5
5	0 58 07	14 13 18	3 46	0 13	1 14	6
6	0 58 06	13 59 56	3 02	0 08	1 14	7
7	0 58 04	13 42 12	2 08	0 04	1 14	7
8	0 58 02	13 21 31	1 08	0 01	1 14	8
9	0 58 01	12 59 40	0 09	0 06	1 14	8
10	0 57 59	12 38 34	0 47	0 10	1 14	9
11	0 57 57	12 19 51	1 35	0 15	1 14	10
12	0 57 55	12 04 52	2 16	0 20	1 14	10
13	0 57 53	11 54 30	2 49	0 24	1 14	11
14	0 57 52	11 49 18	3 14	0 28	1 14	11
15	0 57 50	11 49 25	3 32	0 32	1 14	12
16	0 57 48	11 54 42	3 44	0 36	1 14	13
17	0 57 46	12 04 41	3 48	0 40	1 14	13
18	0 57 45	12 18 38	3 43	0 44	1 14	14
19	0 57 43	12 35 29	3 29	0 47	1 14	14
20	0 57 42	12 53 54	3 04	0 51	1 14	15
21	0 57 41	13 12 24	2 26	0 54	1 14	15
22	0 57 39	13 29 30	1 36	0 58	1 14	16
23	0 57 38	13 43 57	0 37	1 01	1 14	16
24	0 57 37	13 54 58	0 29	1 04	1 14	17
25	0 57 36	14 02 23	1 34	1 07	1 14	17
26	0 57 35	14 06 34	2 34	1 10	1 14	18
27	0 57 34	14 08 15	3 23	1 13	1 14	18
28	0 57 33	14 08 12	3 59	1 16	1 13	18
29	0 57 32	14 07 00	4 21	1 18	1 13	19
30	0 57 32	14 04 47	4 27	1 21	1 13	19
31	0 57 31	14 01 19	4 18	1 24	1 13	20

JUNE

D	☉	☽	☽Dec.	☿	♀	♂
	° ′ ″	° ′ ″	° ′	° ′	° ′	′
1	0 57 30	13 56 00	3 54	1 27	1 13	20
2	0 57 29	13 48 10	3 17	1 29	1 13	21
3	0 57 28	13 37 24	2 29	1 32	1 13	21
4	0 57 28	13 23 40	1 32	1 35	1 13	21
5	0 57 27	13 07 32	0 33	1 37	1 13	22
6	0 57 26	12 50 02	0 25	1 40	1 13	22
7	0 57 25	12 32 29	1 18	1 42	1 13	22
8	0 57 24	12 16 22	2 03	1 45	1 13	23
9	0 57 23	12 03 01	2 39	1 47	1 13	23
10	0 57 22	11 53 33	3 07	1 50	1 13	23
11	0 57 21	11 48 48	3 27	1 52	1 13	24
12	0 57 20	11 49 19	3 40	1 55	1 13	24
13	0 57 19	11 55 19	3 46	1 57	1 13	24
14	0 57 18	12 06 40	3 45	1 59	1 13	25
15	0 57 17	12 22 53	3 35	2 01	1 13	25
16	0 57 16	12 43 00	3 16	2 03	1 13	25
17	0 57 15	13 05 36	2 44	2 05	1 13	26
18	0 57 15	13 28 46	2 00	2 07	1 13	26
19	0 57 14	13 50 22	1 03	2 08	1 13	26
20	0 57 14	14 08 16	0 03	2 09	1 13	27
21	0 57 13	14 20 51	1 13	2 10	1 13	27
22	0 57 13	14 27 21	2 19	2 11	1 13	27
23	0 57 13	14 27 59	3 14	2 11	1 13	27
24	0 57 13	14 23 48	3 55	2 11	1 13	28
25	0 57 13	14 16 18	4 20	2 11	1 13	28
26	0 57 13	14 06 56	4 28	2 11	1 13	28
27	0 57 13	13 56 48	4 21	2 10	1 13	28
28	0 57 13	13 46 28	3 59	2 09	1 13	29
29	0 57 13	13 36 03	3 26	2 08	1 13	29
30	0 57 13	13 25 19	2 42	2 07	1 13	29

JULY

D	☉	☽	☽Dec.	☿	♀	♂
	° ′ ″	° ′ ″	° ′	° ′	° ′	′
1	0 57 13	13 13 54	1 50	2 05	1 13	29
2	0 57 13	13 01 35	0 53	2 04	1 13	30
3	0 57 14	12 48 23	0 04	2 02	1 13	30
4	0 57 13	12 34 40	0 58	2 00	1 13	30
5	0 57 13	12 21 07	1 46	1 58	1 13	30
6	0 57 13	12 08 37	2 26	1 56	1 13	30
7	0 57 13	11 58 09	2 58	1 55	1 13	31
8	0 57 13	11 50 44	3 21	1 53	1 13	31
9	0 57 13	11 47 13	3 36	1 51	1 13	31
10	0 57 13	11 48 19	3 43	1 49	1 13	31
11	0 57 13	11 54 33	3 44	1 47	1 13	31
12	0 57 13	12 06 08	3 37	1 45	1 13	32
13	0 57 13	12 22 56	3 22	1 43	1 13	32
14	0 57 13	12 44 22	2 56	1 41	1 13	32
15	0 57 13	13 09 18	2 19	1 39	1 13	32
16	0 57 14	13 35 55	1 29	1 37	1 12	32
17	0 57 14	14 01 50	0 27	1 35	1 12	33
18	0 57 14	14 24 25	0 42	1 33	1 12	33
19	0 57 15	14 41 09	1 53	1 31	1 12	33
20	0 57 15	14 50 17	2 57	1 29	1 12	33
21	0 57 16	14 51 20	3 47	1 27	1 12	33
22	0 57 16	14 45 01	4 20	1 25	1 12	33
23	0 57 17	14 32 59	4 33	1 23	1 12	34
24	0 57 18	14 17 20	4 29	1 21	1 12	34
25	0 57 19	13 59 59	4 09	1 19	1 12	34
26	0 57 20	13 42 24	3 36	1 17	1 12	34
27	0 57 21	13 25 33	2 53	1 15	1 12	34
28	0 57 22	13 09 52	2 03	1 12	1 12	34
29	0 57 23	12 55 24	1 09	1 10	1 12	35
30	0 57 24	12 42 05	0 13	1 08	1 12	35
31	0 57 25	12 29 47	0 41	1 05	1 12	35

AUGUST

D	☉	☽	☽Dec.	☿	♀	♂
	° ′ ″	° ′ ″	° ′	° ′	° ′	′
1	0 57 26	12 18 27	1 31	1 02	1 12	35
2	0 57 27	12 08 12	2 13	1 00	1 12	35
3	0 57 28	11 59 21	2 47	0 57	1 12	35
4	0 57 29	11 52 19	3 13	0 54	1 12	36
5	0 57 30	11 47 42	3 31	0 51	1 12	36
6	0 57 30	11 46 07	3 40	0 48	1 12	36
7	0 57 31	11 48 13	3 43	0 44	1 12	36
8	0 57 32	11 54 32	3 37	0 41	1 12	36
9	0 57 33	12 05 30	3 24	0 37	1 12	36
10	0 57 34	12 21 17	3 02	0 33	1 12	36
11	0 57 35	12 41 44	2 30	0 29	1 12	37
12	0 57 36	13 06 12	1 48	0 24	1 12	37
13	0 57 37	13 33 23	0 54	0 20	1 11	37
14	0 57 38	14 01 19	0 10	0 15	1 11	37
15	0 57 39	14 27 25	1 20	0 10	1 11	37
16	0 57 40	14 48 51	2 28	0 04	1 11	37
17	0 57 41	15 03 01	3 28	0 01	1 11	37
18	0 57 42	15 08 16	4 12	0 07	1 11	37
19	0 57 44	15 04 17	4 37	0 12	1 11	38
20	0 57 45	14 52 04	4 40	0 18	1 11	38
21	0 57 47	14 33 41	4 24	0 24	1 11	38
22	0 57 49	14 11 33	3 53	0 29	1 11	38
23	0 57 50	13 48 01	3 10	0 35	1 11	38
24	0 57 52	13 24 58	2 18	0 40	1 11	38
25	0 57 54	13 03 42	1 23	0 45	1 11	38
26	0 57 56	12 44 57	0 27	0 49	1 11	38
27	0 57 58	12 29 01	0 28	0 52	1 11	39
28	0 57 59	12 15 54	1 17	0 55	1 11	39
29	0 58 01	12 05 26	2 01	0 56	1 11	39
30	0 58 03	11 57 24	2 37	0 56	1 11	39
31	0 58 05	11 51 38	3 06	0 55	1 11	39

SEPTEMBER

D	☉ ° ′ ″	☽ ° ′ ″	☽Dec. ° ′	☿ ° ′	♀ ° ′	♂ ′
1	0 58 06	11 48 03	3 26	0 53	1 10	39
2	0 58 08	11 46 42	3 38	0 50	1 10	39
3	0 58 09	11 47 44	3 42	0 46	1 10	39
4	0 58 11	11 51 27	3 38	0 40	1 10	39
5	0 58 13	11 58 12	3 27	0 33	1 10	40
6	0 58 14	12 08 22	3 07	0 26	1 10	40
7	0 58 16	12 22 14	2 38	0 18	1 10	40
8	0 58 17	12 39 56	1 59	0 10	1 10	40
9	0 58 19	13 01 16	1 11	0 01	1 10	40
10	0 58 20	13 25 38	0 14	0 08	1 10	40
11	0 58 22	13 51 49	0 50	0 18	1 10	40
12	0 58 23	14 17 57	1 56	0 27	1 10	40
13	0 58 25	14 41 37	2 59	0 35	1 10	40
14	0 58 27	15 00 07	3 52	0 44	1 10	41
15	0 58 28	15 10 59	4 29	0 52	1 09	41
16	0 58 30	15 12 35	4 45	1 00	1 09	41
17	0 58 32	15 04 35	4 40	1 07	1 09	41
18	0 58 34	14 48 05	4 15	1 13	1 09	41
19	0 58 36	14 25 16	3 33	1 19	1 09	41
20	0 58 39	13 58 54	2 41	1 24	1 09	41
21	0 58 41	13 31 39	1 43	1 29	1 09	41
22	0 58 43	13 05 44	0 43	1 33	1 09	41
23	0 58 45	12 42 44	0 14	1 37	1 09	41
24	0 58 48	12 23 32	1 06	1 39	1 09	41
25	0 58 50	12 08 32	1 51	1 42	1 09	42
26	0 58 52	11 57 42	2 29	1 44	1 08	42
27	0 58 54	11 50 45	2 59	1 45	1 08	42
28	0 58 56	11 47 16	3 21	1 46	1 08	42
29	0 58 58	11 46 49	3 36	1 47	1 08	42
30	0 59 01	11 48 55	3 43	1 48	1 08	42

OCTOBER

D	☉ ° ′ ″	☽ ° ′ ″	☽Dec. ° ′	☿ ° ′	♀ ° ′	♂ ′
1	0 59 03	11 53 15	3 41	1 48	1 08	42
2	0 59 05	11 59 32	3 32	1 48	1 08	42
3	0 59 07	12 07 43	3 13	1 48	1 08	42
4	0 59 09	12 17 48	2 46	1 48	1 08	42
5	0 59 10	12 29 56	2 09	1 47	1 07	43
6	0 59 12	12 44 20	1 23	1 47	1 07	43
7	0 59 14	13 01 05	0 30	1 46	1 07	43
8	0 59 16	13 20 08	0 29	1 46	1 07	43
9	0 59 18	13 41 04	1 32	1 45	1 07	43
10	0 59 19	14 03 00	2 32	1 44	1 07	43
11	0 59 21	14 24 27	3 26	1 44	1 06	43
12	0 59 23	14 43 22	4 09	1 43	1 06	43
13	0 59 24	14 57 22	4 37	1 42	1 06	43
14	0 59 26	15 04 11	4 44	1 42	1 06	43
15	0 59 28	15 02 14	4 31	1 41	1 06	43
16	0 59 30	14 51 11	3 59	1 40	1 06	43
17	0 59 33	14 32 07	3 10	1 40	1 05	43
18	0 59 35	14 07 17	2 11	1 39	1 05	44
19	0 59 37	13 39 32	1 08	1 38	1 05	44
20	0 59 39	13 11 41	0 06	1 38	1 05	44
21	0 59 42	12 46 01	0 51	1 37	1 05	44
22	0 59 44	12 24 11	1 40	1 37	1 04	44
23	0 59 46	12 07 07	2 21	1 36	1 04	44
24	0 59 48	11 55 11	2 53	1 36	1 04	44
25	0 59 50	11 48 20	3 17	1 35	1 04	44
26	0 59 53	11 46 11	3 34	1 34	1 03	44
27	0 59 55	11 48 11	3 43	1 34	1 03	44
28	0 59 57	11 53 36	3 45	1 33	1 03	44
29	0 59 59	12 01 40	3 38	1 33	1 03	44
30	1 00 01	12 11 34	3 22	1 33	1 02	44
31	1 00 03	12 22 37	2 57	1 32	1 02	45

NOVEMBER

D	☉ ° ′ ″	☽ ° ′ ″	☽Dec. ° ′	☿ ° ′	♀ ° ′	♂ ′
1	1 00 05	12 34 16	2 22	1 32	1 02	45
2	1 00 06	12 46 12	1 37	1 31	1 01	45
3	1 00 08	12 58 20	0 44	1 31	1 01	45
4	1 00 10	13 10 49	0 14	1 30	1 01	45
5	1 00 11	13 23 55	1 15	1 30	1 00	45
6	1 00 13	13 37 50	2 14	1 29	1 00	45
7	1 00 14	13 52 32	3 07	1 29	0 59	45
8	1 00 15	14 07 34	3 50	1 28	0 59	45
9	1 00 17	14 21 55	4 21	1 28	0 59	45
10	1 00 18	14 33 59	4 37	1 27	0 58	45
11	1 00 20	14 41 48	4 35	1 27	0 58	45
12	1 00 21	14 43 29	4 14	1 26	0 57	45
13	1 00 23	14 37 46	3 36	1 26	0 57	45
14	1 00 25	14 24 29	2 42	1 25	0 56	45
15	1 00 26	14 04 42	1 40	1 24	0 56	45
16	1 00 28	13 40 33	0 34	1 24	0 55	46
17	1 00 30	13 14 36	0 29	1 23	0 54	46
18	1 00 32	12 49 23	1 24	1 22	0 54	46
19	1 00 33	12 26 59	2 10	1 20	0 53	46
20	1 00 35	12 08 54	2 46	1 19	0 53	46
21	1 00 37	11 56 00	3 12	1 18	0 52	46
22	1 00 38	11 48 41	3 31	1 16	0 51	46
23	1 00 40	11 46 54	3 42	1 14	0 50	46
24	1 00 42	11 50 17	3 46	1 12	0 50	46
25	1 00 43	11 58 11	3 43	1 10	0 49	46
26	1 00 45	12 09 41	3 31	1 07	0 48	46
27	1 00 46	12 23 42	3 10	1 04	0 47	46
28	1 00 48	12 38 58	2 38	1 00	0 46	46
29	1 00 49	12 54 15	1 55	0 56	0 45	46
30	1 00 50	13 08 30	1 03	0 51	0 44	46

DECEMBER

D	☉ ° ′ ″	☽ ° ′ ″	☽Dec. ° ′	☿ ° ′	♀ ° ′	♂ ′
1	1 00 51	13 21 01	0 03	0 46	0 43	46
2	1 00 52	13 31 33	0 59	0 40	0 42	46
3	1 00 53	13 40 17	2 00	0 33	0 41	46
4	1 00 54	13 47 44	2 55	0 25	0 40	46
5	1 00 55	13 54 31	3 39	0 16	0 39	46
6	1 00 55	14 01 01	4 11	0 07	0 38	47
7	1 00 56	14 07 13	4 28	0 03	0 36	47
8	1 00 57	14 12 33	4 31	0 14	0 35	47
9	1 00 57	14 15 58	4 17	0 25	0 33	47
10	1 00 58	14 16 08	3 48	0 37	0 32	47
11	1 00 59	14 11 51	3 04	0 48	0 30	47
12	1 00 59	14 02 23	2 08	0 58	0 29	47
13	1 01 00	13 47 52	1 04	1 08	0 27	47
14	1 01 01	13 29 17	0 01	1 15	0 25	47
15	1 01 02	13 08 16	1 01	1 20	0 24	47
16	1 01 03	12 46 48	1 53	1 23	0 22	47
17	1 01 03	12 26 47	2 35	1 22	0 20	47
18	1 01 04	12 09 50	3 06	1 19	0 18	47
19	1 01 05	11 57 13	3 27	1 14	0 16	47
20	1 01 06	11 49 42	3 40	1 06	0 14	47
21	1 01 06	11 47 43	3 46	0 57	0 11	47
22	1 01 07	11 51 19	3 45	0 47	0 09	47
23	1 01 08	12 00 13	3 36	0 36	0 07	47
24	1 01 08	12 13 46	3 19	0 25	0 05	47
25	1 01 09	12 30 59	2 53	0 15	0 02	47
26	1 01 10	12 50 28	2 15	0 05	0 00	47
27	1 01 10	13 10 36	1 27	0 05	0 03	47
28	1 01 10	13 29 36	0 28	0 13	0 05	47
29	1 01 11	13 45 53	0 37	0 21	0 08	47
30	1 01 11	13 58 19	1 42	0 29	0 10	47
31	1 01 11	14 06 28	2 42	0 35	0 13	47

d	h	m			PHENOMENA, 1997
Jan.					
1	1	17	am	☽	on Equator
2	0	00	am	⊕	in Perihelion
7	9	06	pm	☽	Max. Dec.18°S.25′
10	8	43	am	☽	in Perigee
13	10	50	pm	☽	on Equator
19	5	31	am	♀	in ☋
20	8	05	pm	☽	Max. Dec.18°N.22′
24	5	00	am	☿	Gt. Elong.25°W.
25	4	31	pm	☽	in Apogee
28	9	28	am	☽	on Equator
29	1	54	am	♂	in Aphelion
31	7	07	pm	☿	in ☋
Feb.					
4	8	54	am	☽	Max. Dec.18°S.17′
7	8	33	pm	☽	in Perigee
10	8	50	am	☽	on Equator
11	3	19	am	☿	in Aphelion
17	2	39	am	☽	Max. Dec.18°N.13′
21	4	51	pm	☽	in Apogee
23	1	22	am	♀	in Aphelion
24	4	04	pm	☽	on Equator
Mar.					
3	6	13	pm	☽	Max. Dec.18°S.10′
8	8	54	am	☽	in Perigee
9	1	15	am	●	Total Eclipse
9	8	06	pm	☽	on Equator
16	9	32	am	☽	Max. Dec.18°N. 8′
20	1	55	pm	☉	Enters ♈,Equinox
20	11	29	pm	☽	in Apogee
22	11	13	am	☿	in ☊
23	10	16	pm	☽	on Equator
24	4	45	am	◗	Partial Eclipse
27	2	58	am	☿	in Perihelion
31	0	47	am	☽	Max. Dec.18°S. 9′
Apr.					
5	4	42	pm	☽	in Perigee
6	1	00	am	☿	Gt. Elong.19°E.
6	6	52	am	☽	on Equator
12	5	51	pm	☽	Max. Dec.18°N.11′
17	3	20	pm	☽	in Apogee
20	5	23	am	☽	on Equator
27	6	30	am	☽	Max. Dec.18°S.16′
29	6	23	pm	☿	in ☋
May					
3	11	06	am	☽	in Perigee
3	3	52	pm	☽	on Equator
10	2	36	am	☿	in Aphelion
10	3	33	am	☽	Max. Dec.18°N.20′
12	9	03	am	♀	in ☊
15	10	09	am	☽	in Apogee
17	1	58	pm	☽	on Equator
22	11	00	pm	☿	Gt. Elong.25°W.
24	1	34	pm	☽	Max. Dec.18°S.24′
29	6	58	am	☽	in Perigee
30	11	05	pm	☽	on Equator
Jun.					
6	1	26	pm	☽	Max. Dec.18°N.27′
12	5	07	am	☽	in Apogee
13	11	28	pm	☽	on Equator
15	9	31	am	♀	in Perihelion
18	10	29	am	☿	in ☊
20	10	53	pm	☽	Max. Dec.18°S.28′
21	8	20	am	☉	Enters ♋,Solstice
23	2	14	am	☿	in Perihelion
24	5	07	am	☽	in Perigee
27	5	39	am	☽	on Equator
Jul.					
3	10	17	pm	☽	Max. Dec.18°N.27′
4	7	00	pm	⊕	in Aphelion
8	6	20	am	♂	in ☋
9	10	55	pm	☽	in Apogee
11	8	42	am	☽	on Equator
18	9	43	am	☽	Max. Dec.18°S.25′
21	11	07	pm	☽	in Perigee
24	1	02	pm	☽	on Equator
26	5	39	pm	☿	in ☋
31	5	28	am	☽	Max. Dec.18°N.22′
Aug.					
4	0	00	am	☿	Gt. Elong.27°E.
6	1	51	am	☿	in Aphelion
6	1	42	pm	☽	in Apogee
7	4	38	pm	☽	on Equator
14	8	27	pm	☽	Max. Dec.18°S.18′
19	5	09	am	☽	in Perigee
20	10	07	pm	☽	on Equator
27	11	32	am	☽	Max. Dec.18°N.16′
31	10	17	pm	♀	in ☋
Sep.					
1	11	52	pm	●	Partial Eclipse
2	9	33	pm	☽	in Apogee
3	11	08	pm	☽	on Equator
11	5	30	am	☽	Max. Dec.18°S.15′
14	9	45	am	☿	in ☊
16	3	28	pm	☽	in Perigee
16	6	50	pm	◗	Total Eclipse
16	10	00	pm	☿	Gt. Elong.18°W.
17	8	46	am	☽	on Equator
19	1	29	am	☿	in Perihelion
22	11	56	pm	☉	Enters ♎,Equinox
23	5	56	pm	☽	Max. Dec.18°N.15′
29	11	44	pm	☽	in Apogee
Oct.					
1	5	05	am	☽	on Equator
5	4	58	pm	♀	in Aphelion
8	0	23	pm	☽	Max. Dec.18°S.18′
14	7	50	pm	☽	on Equator
15	2	09	am	☽	in Perigee
21	2	11	am	☽	Max. Dec.18°N.22′
22	4	54	pm	☿	in ☋
27	9	12	am	☽	in Apogee
28	11	52	am	☽	on Equator
Nov.					
2	1	07	am	☿	in Aphelion
4	6	18	pm	☽	Max. Dec.18°S.28′
6	7	00	am	♀	Gt. Elong.47°E.
11	5	47	am	☽	on Equator
12	8	02	am	☽	in Perigee
17	0	32	pm	☽	Max. Dec.18°N.33′
24	2	30	am	☽	in Apogee
24	8	17	pm	☽	on Equator
28	4	00	pm	☿	Gt. Elong.22°E.
Dec.					
2	1	20	am	☽	Max. Dec.18°S.38′
8	1	43	pm	☽	on Equator
9	5	03	pm	☽	in Perigee
11	9	00	am	☿	in ☊
11	11	00	pm	♀	Gt. Brilliance
14	11	37	pm	☽	Max. Dec.18°N.40′
16	0	44	am	☿	in Perihelion
21	8	07	pm	☉	Enters ♑,Solstice
21	11	24	pm	☽	in Apogee
22	5	57	am	☽	on Equator
23	1	47	am	♀	in ☊
29	10	41	am	☽	Max. Dec.18°S.40′

Showing the approximate time when each Aspect is formed.
am denotes morning; pm denotes afternoon.
Note:- Semi-quintile, or 36° apart, ⊥; Bi-quintile, or 144° ±; Quincunx or 150° ∇
☽☌● Eclipse of ☉. ☽☍☉ Eclipse of ☽. ☌ Occultation by ☽.

JANUARY

Day	Aspect	Time		
1 W	☽☌♂	1am	2	B
	☽☍♄	5	13	B
	☽△♅	9	6	G
	☽✱♇	11	19	G
	☽P♄	11	31	B
	☿P♆	5pm	1	
	♀⊥♃	5	1	
	☽P♂	5	58	B
2 TH	☉☌☿	1am	22	
	☽□☿	1	41	B
	☽□☉	1	45	B
	☽∠♇	4pm	51	b
	☽✱♀	7	17	G
	♀⊥♆	11	5	
	☿⊥♇	11	11	
3 F	☽□♃	4am	50	B
	☽□♆	7	11	B
	☽P♇	10	0	D
	☽⚺♂	1pm	9	g
	☽□♅	7	28	B
	☽⚺♇	9	26	g
4 S	☽∠♀	2am	45	b
	☽✱☿	5	26	G
	☽✱☉	3pm	34	G
	☽∠♂	5	35	b
	☽⚼♄	7	35	b
	☉P♀	8	6	
5 SU	☽∠☿	6am	17	b
	☽⚺♀	8	45	g
	☽✱♃	0pm	50	G
	☽✱♆	2	12	G
	☽∠☉	8	25	b
	☽✱♂	8	49	G
	☽△♄	10	14	G
6 M	☽✱♅	1am	37	G
	☽☌♇	3	21	D
	☽⚺☿	6	31	g
	☽∠♃	3pm	10	b
	☽∠♆	4	7	b
7 TU	☽⚺☉	0am	0	g
	☽∠♅	3	9	b
	♀⚺♃	2pm	20	
	☽⚺♃	4	33	g
	☽☌♀	4	43	G
	☽⚺♆	5	8	g
	♀⚺♆	9	40	
8 W	☽□♂	0am	13	B
	☽□♄	0	43	B
	☽⚺♅	3	53	g
	☽⚺♇	5	25	g
	☽☌☿	5	27	G
	☿⚺♇	6	14	
	♀⊥♅	9	9	
9 TH	☽☌☉	4	26	D
	☽∠♇	5	33	b
	♂☍♄	10	53	
	♃☌♆	11	40	
	☿⚺♅	3pm	38	
	☽☌♆	5	29	D
	☽☌♃	5	33	G
	☽⚺♀	9	19	g

Day	Aspect	Time		
	☉∠♇	9	20	
10 F	☽✱♄	0am	56	G
	☽△♂	1	8	G
	☉Q♄	1	42	
	☽⚺☿	3	35	g
	☽☌♅	4	0	B
	☽✱♇	5	25	G
	☽∠♀	11pm	18	b
11 S	☽∠♄	0am	52	b
	☽⚼♂	1	24	b
	☽∠☿	2	55	b
	☽⚺☉	7	35	g
	☿P♆	1pm	57	
	☽⚺♆	5	23	g
	☽⚺♃	6	6	g
	♀□♄	7	16	
	☽P♇	10	46	D
12 SU	☽⚺♄	1am	3	g
	☽✱♀	1	33	G
	☽✱☿	2	43	G
	☽⚺♅	4	9	g
	☽□♇	5	31	B
	♀□♂	6	36	
	☽∠☉	9	34	b
	☿☌♀	2pm	31	
	☽∠♆	5	48	b
	☽∠♃	6	52	b
	☿ Stat	8	41	
13 M	☽∠♅	4am	51	b
	♀⚺♅	9	41	
	☽✱☉	0pm	11	G
	☽P♂	2	42	B
	☽P♄	3	58	B
	☽✱♆	6	49	G
	☽✱♃	8	16	G
14 TU	♀⚺♇	1am	24	
	☽☌♄	2	58	B
	☽☍♂	4	30	B
	☽□☿	4	37	B
	☽P♄	5	40	B
	☽✱♅	6	12	G
	☽P♂	6	46	B
	☽△♇	7	32	G
	☽□♀	8	7	B
	☽⚼♇	9	36	b
15 W	☿P♃	1pm	3	
	☽□☉	8	2	B
	☽□♆	11	0	B
16 TH	☽□♃	1am	19	B
	☽P♇	1	35	D
	☽⚺♄	7	47	g
	☉P☿	7	59	
	☽△☿	10	31	G
	☽□♅	11	8	B
	☽△♀	6pm	28	G
17 F	☿⚺♅	5am	59	
	☉P♃	8	1	
	☽∠♄	11	19	b
	☉☌♆	0pm	34	
	☽⚼♂	1	56	b
	☽⚼☿	3	5	b
18 S	☽⚼♀	1am	6	b
	☽△♆	6	8	G

Day	Aspect	Time		
	☽△☉	7	36	G
	☽△♃	9	27	G
	☿⚺♇	11	34	
	☽✱♄	3pm	32	G
	☽△♂	6	29	G
	☽△♅	6	59	G
	☽☍♇	8	12	B
	♀⊥♇	10	59	
19 SU	☽⚼♆	10am	41	b
	☉☌♃	1pm	7	
	☽⚼♃	2	31	b
	☽⚼☉	2	36	b
	☉P♆	2	39	
	☽⚼♅	11	49	b
20	♂△♅	6	56	
21 TU	☽□♄	1am	39	B
	☽□♂	5	14	B
	☽☍☿	10	28	B
22 W	☽☍♀	1	37	B
	☉P♅	2	8	
	♂P♄	4	24	
	☽⚼♇	11	55	b
	☉✱♄	6pm	31	
23 TH	☽☍♆	3am	9	B
	☽☍♃	8	39	B
	☽△♄	1pm	33	G
	☽☍☉	3	11	B
	☽☍♅	5	0	B
	☽✱♂	5	38	G
	☽△♇	5	58	G
24 F	☉☌♅	1	53	
	☽⚼♄	8	1	b
25 S	☽∠♂	0am	17	b
	☉△♂	0	25	
	☉✱♇	0	38	
	♂✱♇	2	20	
	☿⊥♇	0pm	18	
	☽⚼☿	0	31	b
	☽P♇	10	8	D
26 SU	☽⚼♀	6am	49	b
	☽□♇	6	50	B
	♀∠♇	6	58	
	☽⚺♂	7	6	g
	♂P♄	8	59	
	☽△☿	10pm	9	G
	☽⚼♆	10	29	b
27 M	☿P♀	1am	50	
	♀Q♄	3	2	
	☽⚼♃	5	38	b
	☽⚼♅	0pm	42	b
	☽△♀	4	56	G
	☽⚼☉	6	58	b
28 TU	☽P♂	4am	15	B
	☽P♄	4	24	B
	☽△♆	5	1	G
	♃P♆	5	9	
	☽△♃	0pm	37	G
	☽P♄	2	24	B
	☽P♂	2	37	B
	☽☍♄	4	0	B
	☽△♅	7	10	G
	☽✱♇	7	46	G
	☽☌♂	8	28	B

Day	Aspect	Time		
29 W	☽△☉	4am	1	G
	☽□☿	5pm	12	B
30 TH	☽∠♇	1am	40	b
	☽□♀	11	49	B
	☽□♆	4pm	49	B
	☽P♇	7	27	D
31 F	☽□♃	1am	4	B
	☽□♅	6	27	B
	☽⚺♇	6	50	g
	☽⚺♂	7	48	g
	☽□☉	7pm	40	B

FEBRUARY

Day	Aspect	Time		
1 S	☽⚼♄	8am	5	b
	☽✱☿	9	14	G
	☽∠♂	0pm	6	b
	♀☌♆	2	28	
2 SU	☽✱♆	1am	18	G
	☽✱♀	2	24	G
	☿∠♇	3	53	
	☽✱♃	9	48	G
	☽△♄	11	32	G
	☽✱♅	2pm	3	G
	☽☌♇	2	15	D
	☽✱♂	3	17	G
	☽∠☿	3	21	b
	☽P☉	3	45	G
3 M	☽∠♆	3am	57	b
	☽✱☉	6	22	G
	☽∠♀	7	34	b
	☿Q♄	8	22	
	☽∠♃	0pm	30	b
	☽∠♅	4	15	b
	☽⚺☿	8	5	g
4 TU	☽⚺♆	5am	35	g
	☽∠☉	9	47	b
	☽⚺♀	11	26	g
	☽⚺♃	2pm	11	g
	☽□♄	3	17	B
	☽⚺♅	5	29	g
	☽⚺♇	5	32	g
	☽□♂	6	32	B
5 W	♅✱♇	10am	48	
	☽⚺☉	0pm	10	g
	☽∠♇	5	56	b
	♀P♆	6	18	
6 TH	♂ Stat	0am	38	
	♀☌♃	1	48	
	☉Q♇	2	13	
	☽☌☿	2	17	G
	☽☌♆	6	29	D
	♀✱♄	11	34	
	☽P☉	0pm	7	G
	☽☌♃	3	17	G
	☽✱♄	3	55	G
	☽☌♀	4	16	G
	☽✱♇	5	48	G
	☽☌♅	5	53	B
	☽△♂	6	43	G
7 F	♀✱♇	11am	6	
	♀☌♅	0pm	44	
	♀P♃	1	12	
	☽☌☉	3	6	D

Day	Aspect	Time		
	☽∠♄	3	40	b
	☽⚼♂	6	16	b
	♀△♂	9	33	
8 S	☉∠♄	0am	22	
	☿☌♆	0	31	
	♀P♅	5	35	
	☽⚺♆	5	49	g
	☽⚺☿	6	21	g
	☽P♇	10	6	D
	☽⚺♃	3pm	12	g
	☽⚺♄	3	24	g
	☽□♇	5	2	B
	☽⚺♅	5	15	g
	☽⚺♀	7	41	g
9 SU	☽∠♆	5am	35	b
	☽∠☿	8	34	b
	☉⚼♂	1pm	24	
	☽∠♃	3	25	b
	♃✱♄	3	32	
	☽∠♅	5	13	b
	☽⚺☉	5	58	g
	☽∠♀	9	49	b
10 M	☽P♂	4am	0	B
	☽✱♆	5	46	G
	☽P♄	7	30	B
	☽P♄	10	9	B
	☽✱☿	11	24	G
	☽P♂	1pm	46	B
	☽☌♄	3	56	B
	☽✱♃	4	10	G
	☽△♇	5	21	G
	☽✱♅	5	43	G
	☽☍♂	5	58	B
	☽∠☉	8	13	b
11 TU	☽✱♀	0am	39	G
	☽⚼♇	6pm	28	b
	☽✱☉	11	22	G
12 W	♂△♅	0am	6	
	♃P♅	1	56	
	☽□♆	8	10	B
	☽P♇	9	57	D
	☿✱♄	11	33	
	☿☌♃	6pm	22	
	☽⚺♄	7	17	g
	☽□♃	7	59	B
	☽□☿	8	9	B
	☽□♅	8	59	B
	☿✱♇	10	47	
13 TH	☿△♂	1am	29	
	☿☌♅	3	57	
	☽□♀	9	28	B
	☽P☉	4pm	50	G
	☿P♆	6	45	
	☽∠♄	10	18	b
	☽⚼♂	11	27	b
14 F	♃✱♇	0am	41	
	♂△♃	5	7	
	☽□☉	8	58	B
	♂✱♇	1pm	5	
	☽△♆	2	4	G
15 S	☽✱♄	2am	16	G
	☽△♂	2	58	G
	☽☍♇	3	6	B

Date	Aspect	Hour	Min	
	☽△♃	3	34	G
	☽△♅	3	52	G
	☽△☿	10	7	G
	☽P♀	1pm	11	G
	☽⚼♆	6	22	b
	☽△♀	11	5	G
	☿P♅	11	36	
16 SU	♃☌♅	2am	22	
	☽⚼♅	8	36	b
	☽⚼♃	8	41	b
	☿P♃	0pm	18	
	♂☍♄	5	14	
	☽⚼☿	7	0	b
	☽△☉	10	56	G
17 M	♀Q♇	3am	51	
	☉⊻♆	4	54	
	☽⚼♀	7	28	b
	☽□♂	0pm	11	B
	☽□♄	0	35	B
	☉±♂	4	20	
	☉⊥♄	10	50	
18 TU	☽⚼☉	7am	11	b
	☽⚼♇	6pm	49	b
19 W	♀⚼♂	0am	53	
	☽☍♆	11	9	B
	♀∠♄	1pm	40	
	☽P♀	2	46	G
	♄△♇	4	43	
	☽⚹♂	11	18	G
20 TH	☽△♇	1am	1	G
	☽△♄	1	5	G
	☽☍♅	2	16	B
	☽☍♃	3	41	B
	☿Q♇	5pm	13	
21 F	☽☍☿	2am	36	B
	☽∠♂	5	12	b
	☽⚼♄	7	45	b
	☽☍♀	0pm	17	B
	☽P☉	5	4	G
	☿⚼♂	7	43	
22 S	☽P♇	5am	3	D
	☽☍☉	10	27	B
	☽⊻♂	11	9	g
	☽□♇	1pm	54	B
	☉∇♂	5	21	
	☿∠♄	6	15	
23 SU	☽⚼♆	6am	36	b
	☉⊥♆	8	40	
	☽⚼♅	9pm	56	b
24 M	☽⚼♃	0am	41	b
	☉□♇	3	17	
	☽P♂	3	38	B
	☽△♆	1pm	0	G
	☽P♄	1	38	B
	☉⊻♄	3	41	
	☽P♄	6	34	B
	☽☌♂	10	40	B
	☉⊻♅	11	35	
25 TU	☽⚹♇	2am	33	G
	☽☍♄	3	42	B
	☽△♅	4	16	G
	☽P♂	5	10	B
	♀±♂	5	11	
	☽△♃	7	25	G
	☽⚼☿	0pm	21	b
	☽⚼♀	5	51	b
26 W	☉P♇	1am	29	
	♀⊻♆	6	17	
	☽∠♇	8	26	b
	☽⚼☉	1pm	11	b
	☿±♂	1	15	
	☉⊻♃	9	53	
	☽△☿	10	52	G
	☽P☉	11	29	G
27 TH	☽□♆	0am	47	B
	☽P♇	1	52	D
	☽△♀	2	49	G
	☽⊻♂	8	48	g
	♀⊥♄	11	45	
	☿⊻♆	0pm	46	
	☽⊻♇	1	47	g
	☽□♅	3	39	B
	☽□♃	7	30	B
	☽△☉	8	59	G
28 F	☽P♀	4am	12	G
	☿⊥♄	11	1	
	☽P☿	0pm	41	G
	☽∠♂	0	58	b
	☽⚼♄	8	17	b
MARCH				
1 S	♀∇♂	4am	7	
	☽⚹♆	10	6	G
	☿∇♂	0pm	48	
	♄⚹♅	1	24	
	☽⚹♂	4	21	G
	☽□☿	5	0	B
	☽□♀	5	57	B
	☽☌♇	10	17	D
2 SU	☽⚹♅	0am	15	G
	☽△♄	0	18	G
	☽⚹♃	4	36	G
	☽□☉	9	38	B
	☽∠♆	1pm	29	b
	☿☌♀	2	32	
3 M	☿⊥♆	0am	12	
	☽∠♅	3	12	b
	♀⊥♆	4	27	
	☉⊥♅	6	45	
	☽∠♃	7	44	b
	☿□♇	8	0	
	♀□♇	3pm	31	
	☽⊻♆	3	58	g
	☽□♂	8	33	B
	☿⊻♅	11	39	
4 TU	☿⊻♄	1am	59	
	☽⊻♇	3	15	g
	☽⚹♀	4	23	G
	☽⊻♅	5	16	g
	☽□♄	5	35	B
	☽⚹☿	6	4	G
	☽⊻♃	9	58	g
	☉∠♆	2pm	33	
	♀⊻♅	2	39	
	☽⚹☉	5	48	G
	♀⊻♄	7	3	
5 W	☽∠♇	4am	28	b
	☽∠♀	7	56	b
	☽∠☿	10	47	b
	☿P♀	11	8	
	☿⊻♃	3pm	47	
	☽☌♆	6	26	D
	☽∠☉	8	24	b
	☽△♂	9	34	G
6 TH	☽⚹♇	5am	0	G
	☽☌♅	7	4	B
	☽⚹♄	7	36	G
	☽⊻♀	10	37	g
	☽☌♃	0pm	4	G
	☉⊥♃	0	56	
	☽⊻☿	2	36	g
	☽⚼♂	9	12	b
	☽⊻☉	10	19	g
7 F	☿P♇	1am	11	
	♀⊻♃	7	15	
	☽∠♄	7	47	b
	☿⊥♅	8	20	
	☽⊻♆	6pm	36	g
	☽P♀	9	46	G
	☽P♇	10	9	D
8 S	☿∠♆	0am	4	
	♀P♇	1	7	
	☽P☿	2	48	G
	☽□♇	4	49	B
	☽⊻♅	6	59	g
	☽⊻♄	7	44	g
	☽⊻♃	0pm	25	g
	♇Stat	0	54	
	☽☌♀	2	36	G
	☽∠♆	6	23	b
	☽P☉	8	20	G
	☽☌☿	8	56	G
9 SU	☽•●	1am	15	D
	☽P♂	2	5	B
	☽∠♅	6	49	b
	☿⊥♃	6	51	
	☽∠♃	0pm	33	b
	♀⊥♅	2	40	
	☽P♄	2	59	B
	☽⚹♆	6	16	G
	☽☍♂	6	59	B
10 M	☽P♄	1am	21	B
	☽△♇	4	32	G
	☽⚹♅	6	54	G
	☽☌♄	7	55	B
	☽⚹♃	1pm	0	G
	♀∠♆	1	30	
	☽P♂	3	30	B
	☽P☉	4	24	G
	☽⊻♀	6	59	g
	♂△♆	9	58	
	☉P♂	11	54	
11 TU	☽P☿	1am	1	G
	☽⊻☿	4	19	g
	☽⚼♇	4	58	b
	☽⊻☉	5	5	g
	☽P♀	10	4	G
	☉☌☿	3pm	34	
	☽P♇	7	22	D
	☽□♆	7	23	B
	☽∠♀	10	11	b
12 W	☿∠♅	4am	36	
	☽∠☉	8	7	b
	☽□♅	8	46	B
	☽∠☿	9	25	b
	☽⊻♄	10	6	g
	☽□♃	3pm	49	B
	☉∠♅	5	29	
	☿P♂	6	7	
	☽⚼♂	7	41	b
13 TH	♀⊥♃	1am	54	
	☽⚹♀	2	25	G
	☽⚹☉	0pm	14	G
	☽∠♄	0	26	b
	☽⚹☿	3	54	G
	☽△♂	9	24	G
	☽△♆	11	34	G
14 F	☽☍♇	10am	57	B
	☿∠♃	11	39	
	☽△♅	2pm	2	G
	☽⚹♄	3	47	G
	☉P☿	3	53	
	☽△♃	10	17	G
15 S	☿☍♂	0am	6	
	☽⚼♆	3	7	b
	☽P♃	9	17	G
	☽□♀	2pm	44	B
	☽⚼♅	6	8	b
	☿P♄	7	14	
	☿⚹♆	8	30	
16 SU	☽□☉	0am	6	B
	☽⚼♃	3	3	b
	☽□♂	3	31	B
	☽□☿	9	44	B
	♂⚼♃	1pm	23	
	♀P♂	3	17	
17 M	☽□♄	1am	24	B
	♀∠♅	2	27	
	☉P♄	2	50	
	☉☍♂	7	55	
	☽P♃	1pm	26	G
	☉∠♃	9	42	
18 TU	☽⚼♇	1am	15	b
	☉P☿	5	11	
	☽△♀	7	54	G
	☽⚹♂	0pm	42	G
	☽△☉	4	20	G
	☿P♄	6	21	
	☽☍♆	7	0	B
	☿△♇	11	17	
19 W	☽△♇	7am	22	G
	☽△☿	9	1	G
	☽☍♅	11	14	B
	☽△♄	1pm	59	G
	☽⚼♀	5	41	b
	☽∠♂	6	0	b
	♀☍♂	8	8	
	☽☍♃	9	54	B
	☿⚹♅	10	30	
20 TH	☉⚹♆	0am	52	
	☽⚼☉	1	27	b
	☿P♀	4	57	
	☿☌♄	4pm	15	
	☽⚼♄	8	46	b
	☽⚼☿	9	37	b
	☽⊻♂	11	31	g
21 F	☽P♇	0	22	D
	♀∠♃	4	30	
	☽□♇	8	16	B
	☿Q♆	11	5	
22 S	☽P♂	11am	15	B
	♀P♄	1pm	13	
	☽P☿	1	32	G
	☽⚼♆	2	26	b
	♀⚹♆	8	12	
	☿⚹♃	9	23	
23 SU	☿P♂	0am	2	
	☽⚼♅	6	48	b
	☽☌♂	10	21	B
	☽P♄	11	29	B
	☉P♀	0pm	11	
	☽P☉	2	36	G
	☽P♀	3	17	G
	☽⚼♃	6	34	b
	☽△♆	8	40	G
	☽☍♀	11	27	B
24 M	☽P♀	3am	35	G
	☽•☉	4	45	B
	☽P☉	7	41	G
	☽⚹♇	8	37	G
	☽P♄	9	17	B
	☽△♅	0pm	54	G
	☽☍♄	4	26	B
25 TU	☽△♃	0am	52	G
	☉P♄	0	54	
	☽☍☿	9	28	B
	☽P♂	11	14	B
	☽∠♇	2pm	14	b
	♂Q♇	5	49	
	☽⊻♂	8	1	g
26 W	☉△♇	3am	24	
	☽P☿	4	48	G
	☽P♇	6	34	D
	☿Q♅	6	58	
	☽□♆	7	55	B
	☿P♇	11	43	
	☿⚼♇	5pm	3	
	☽⊻♇	7	20	g
	☽□♅	11	41	B
27 TH	☽∠♂	0am	13	b
	☽□♃	11	56	B
	♀△♇	3pm	35	
	♂⚼♅	4	51	
	☿∇♂	10	51	
28 F	☽⚼♀	0am	47	b
	☽⚼☉	3	39	b
	☽⚹♂	3	54	G
	☽⚼♄	8	12	b
	☉⚹♅	11	30	
	☽⚹♆	4pm	59	G
29 S	☽☌♇	3am	49	D
	☽△♀	7	39	G
	☽⚹♅	8	11	G
	☽△☉	9	48	G
	☽P♃	11	20	G
	☽△♄	0pm	14	G
	☽⚼☿	0	48	b
	♀⚹♅	1	17	
	♀P♄	6	18	
	☽⚹♃	8	32	G
	☽∠♆	8	36	b
30 SU	☿Q♃	8am	50	
	☽□♂	9	35	B
	☽∠♅	11	28	b
	☽△☿	7pm	31	G
	☉☌♄	10	20	
	☿±♂	11	20	
	☽⊻♆	11	33	g
	☽∠♃	11	49	b
31 M	☽⊻♇	9am	44	g
	♀☌♄	0pm	48	
	☽⊻♅	2	5	g
	☽□♄	6	18	B
	☽□♀	6	47	B
	☽□☉	7	38	B
APRIL				
1 TU	☽⊻♃	2am	24	g
	☿±♇	4	20	
	☿□♆	8	39	
	☉Q♆	9	40	
	☽∠♇	11	43	b
	☽△♂	0pm	55	G
	♂±♃	2	27	
	☽P♃	3	16	G

Day	Aspect	Time	Min	
	♀Q♆	3	31	
2	☽☌♆	3am	30	D
W	☽□☿	5	30	B
	☽✱♇	1pm	7	G
	☉☌♀	1	45	
	☽⚼♂	1	45	b
	☽☌♅	5	25	B
	☽P☿	7	13	G
	☽✱♄	9	47	G
3	☽✱☉	2am	22	G
TH	☽✱♀	2	36	G
	☽☌♃	5	44	G
	☽∠♄	10pm	46	b
4	☽∠☉	4am	49	b
F	☽⊻♆	5	17	g
	☽∠♀	5	34	b
	☽P♇	9	1	D
	☽✱☿	11	42	G
	☽□♇	2pm	30	B
	☽⊻♅	6	50	g
	☽P♂	7	0	B
	♀✱♃	8	29	
	☽P☉	11	20	G
	☽⊻♄	11	23	g
5	☽P♀	3am	45	G
S	☽∠♆	5	41	b
	☽⊻☉	6	55	g
	☽⊻♃	7	18	g
	☽⊻♀	8	9	g
	☉✱♃	1pm	40	
	☽∠☿	1	55	b
	☽☍♂	2	0	B
	☿⚼♂	2	58	
	☽P♄	6	48	B
	☽∠♅	7	10	b
6	☿⚻♇	2am	32	
SU	☽✱♆	5	57	G
	☽∠♃	7	50	b
	☽△♇	3pm	1	G
	☽⊻☿	3	52	g
	☽P♄	7	13	B
	☽✱♅	7	30	G
7	☽•♄	0am	23	B
M	☽✱♃	8	29	G
	☽☌☉	11	2	D
	☽•♀	1pm	16	G
	☉P♂	1	45	
	☽⚼♇	3	26	b
	☽P♀	5	3	G
	☿P♃	6	43	
	♀⚻♂	6	45	
	☽P♂	8	10	B
	☽P☉	8	41	G
8	☽P♇	4am	57	D
TU	☽□♆	7	1	B
	♀Q♅	11	24	
	☽⚼♂	2pm	11	b
	♀⚼♇	2	28	
	☽☌☿	8	2	G
	☉⚻♂	8	41	
	☽□♅	9	1	B
	♀P♂	11	44	
9	☽⊻♄	2am	26	g
W	☽□♃	11	2	B
	☽△♂	3pm	8	G
	☽⊻☉	4	53	g
	☿□♅	7	48	
	☽⊻♀	8	20	g
10	☉Q♅	1am	22	

Day	Aspect	Time	Min	
TH	☉⚼♇	3	32	
	☽∠♄	4	24	b
	☽△♆	10	10	G
	☽P♃	6pm	45	G
	☽☍♇	7	50	B
	☽∠☉	9	8	b
11	☽△♅	1am	5	G
F	☽∠♀	1	19	b
	☽⊻☿	2	9	g
	☽✱♄	7	15	G
	☽P☿	10	58	G
	☽⚼♆	0pm	59	b
	☉P♇	3	9	
	☽△♃	4	36	G
	☽□♂	7	27	B
	♀±♂	8	37	
	♀P♇	10	21	
12	☽✱☉	2am	33	G
S	☽⚼♅	4	29	b
	☽∠☿	6	18	b
	☽✱♀	7	34	G
	♄Q♆	7pm	8	
	☽⚼♃	8	51	b
	☉P♀	10	24	
13	☽✱☿	11am	13	G
SU	☽□♄	3pm	54	B
	☉±♂	9	18	
	☽P☿	9	39	G
14	☽✱♂	3am	31	G
M	☽⚼♇	8	2	b
	♃Q♇	8	15	
	☽□☉	5pm	0	B
	☽P♃	10	15	G
	☽□♀	11	53	B
15	☿Stat	0am	0	
TU	☽☍♆	3	7	B
	☽∠♂	8	49	b
	☽△♇	1pm	48	G
	♀±♇	6	22	
	☽☍♅	8	8	B
	☽□☿	10	39	B
	♀Q♃	11	46	
16	☽△♄	4am	1	G
W	♀□♆	7	35	
	♂⚻♃	11	13	
	☽⊻♂	2pm	41	g
	☽☍♃	2	46	B
17	☽P♀	2am	17	G
TH	☽P☉	5	31	G
	☽⚼♄	10	47	b
	☽△☉	10	51	G
	☽△♀	7pm	33	G
	☽P♇	9	1	D
18	☽□♇	2am	30	B
F	☽P♂	4	47	B
	♀⚼♂	6	38	
	☽△☿	10	27	G
	☽⚼☉	8pm	4	b
	☽⚼♆	10	16	b
19	☽☌♂	2am	56	B
S	☉±♇	3	56	
	☽⚼♀	5	31	b
	☽P♄	10	17	B
	☽⚼♅	3pm	29	b
	☽⚼☿	3	49	b
	☉□♆	11	2	
20	☿□♅	0am	49	
SU	☉Q♃	3	22	
	☽△♆	4	27	G

Day	Aspect	Time	Min	
	☽⚼♃	10	51	b
	♀⚻♇	0pm	56	
	☽✱♇	2	46	G
	☽△♅	9	25	G
21	☽P♄	0am	44	B
M	☽☍♄	6	8	B
	☽⊻♂	2pm	8	g
	☽△♃	4	44	G
	☽∠♇	8	11	b
22	☉⚼♂	0am	58	
TU	☽P♂	4	36	B
	☿P♃	4	41	
	☿☌♀	6	55	
	☽P♇	11	49	D
	☽□♆	3pm	11	B
	☽∠♂	6	56	b
	☽☍☉	8	33	B
23	☽⊻♇	0am	58	g
W	☽☍☿	4	9	B
	♀□♅	6	56	
	☽□♅	7	31	B
	☽☍♀	7	34	B
	☽P☉	7pm	57	G
	☽✱♂	11	9	G
24	☽□♃	2am	32	B
TH	☽P♀	7	29	G
	☽P☿	2pm	28	G
	☽⚼♄	8	28	b
	☽✱♆	11	26	G
25	☽P♃	0am	19	G
F	☉⚻♇	4	26	
	☿P♀	7	1	
	☽☌♇	8	41	D
	☉☌☿	10	32	
	☽✱♅	3pm	7	G
	☿⚻♇	7	50	
26	☽△♄	0am	1	G
S	☽∠♆	2	41	b
	☽□♂	5	56	B
	☽✱♃	9	51	G
	☽⚼☿	10	59	b
	☽⚼☉	2pm	13	b
	☽∠♅	6	7	b
	☉P☿	8	41	
27	☽⚼♀	2am	22	b
SU	☽⊻♆	5	27	g
	♀⊻♄	10	38	
	☽△☿	0pm	21	G
	☽∠♃	0	45	b
	☽⊻♇	2	17	g
	☽△☉	6	50	G
	♂Stat	7	9	
	☽⊻♅	8	39	g
28	♀P♃	2am	32	
M	☽□♄	5	40	B
	☽△♀	7	21	G
	☽△♂	10	54	G
	☽⊻♃	3pm	13	g
	☽∠♇	4	27	b
	☉□♅	8	44	
29	☽P♀	7am	1	G
TU	☽☌♆	9	46	D
	☽P♃	0pm	36	G
	☽⚼♂	0	51	B
	☽⚼☿	2	11	B
	☽✱♇	6	15	G
	☽P☉	9	19	G
	♀△♂	11	32	
30	☽☌♅	0am	35	B

Day	Aspect	Time	Min	
W	☽□☉	2	37	B
	☽✱♄	9	45	G
	☽□♀	3pm	54	B
	☽☌♃	7	4	G
	☽P☿	7	41	G
	☿⚼♂	8	30	

MAY

Day	Aspect	Time	Min	
1	☿Q♃	7am	52	
TH	☽∠♄	11	20	b
	☽⊻♆	0pm	46	g
	☽✱☿	3	10	G
	☽P♇	5	55	D
	☽□♇	8	59	B
	♆Stat	11	29	
2	☽P♂	1am	54	B
F	☽⊻♅	3	19	g
	♀□♃	7	43	
	☽✱☉	8	57	G
	☽⊻♄	0pm	42	g
	☉P♃	1	28	
	☽∠♆	1	54	b
	☽∠☿	3	28	b
	☽☍♂	5	8	B
	♀⊥♄	7	40	
	☽P♄	8	49	B
	☽⊻♃	9	51	g
	☽✱♀	11	4	G
3	☽∠♅	4am	23	b
S	☽∠☉	11	47	b
	☽✱♆	2pm	55	G
	☽⊻☿	3	46	g
	☽△♇	10	59	G
	☽∠♃	11	2	b
4	☽∠♀	2am	23	b
SU	☽✱♅	5	22	G
	☽P♄	11	17	B
	☽⊻☉	2pm	34	g
	☽•♄	3	6	B
	☉⊻♄	11	20	
	☽⚼♇	11	56	b
5	☽✱♃	0am	14	G
M	☽P♂	4	39	B
	☿□♆	5	43	
	☽⊻♀	5	45	g
	☽P♇	1pm	38	D
	☽•☿	4	48	G
	☽□♆	5	0	B
	☽⚼♂	8	39	b
	☽P☿	10	55	G
6	☽□♅	7am	41	B
TU	♀P♅	8	23	
	☽⊻♄	5pm	59	g
	☽☌☉	8	47	D
	☽△♂	10	18	G
7	☽□♃	3am	20	B
W	☽☌♀	1pm	35	G
	☽P♃	4	32	G
	☽⊻☿	7	29	g
	☽∠♄	8	4	b
	☽△♆	8	15	G
	☉△♂	9	30	
8	☽☍♇	4am	34	B
TH	☽△♅	11	35	G
	☽P☉	3pm	27	G
	☿Stat	6	5	
	☽∠☿	9	56	b
	☽⚼♆	10	46	b
	☽✱♄	10	49	G

Day	Aspect	Time	Min	
9	☽□♂	3am	22	B
F	☽⊻☉	5	25	g
	☽△♃	8	36	G
	☽⚼♅	2pm	34	b
	♀P♆	3	4	
10	☽⊻♀	0am	37	g
S	☽✱☿	1	22	G
	☿⊻♀	9	6	
	☽∠☉	11	13	b
	☽⚼♃	0pm	27	b
	♀△♆	4	7	
	♀∠♄	8	50	
11	☽P☉	3am	24	G
SU	☉□♃	5	16	
	☽□♄	6	52	B
	☽∠♀	7	52	b
	☽✱♂	11	53	G
	☽⚼♇	3pm	17	b
	☽✱☉	6	8	G
	☉⊥♄	11	41	
12	☿□♆	4am	16	
M	☽☍♆	11	24	B
	☽□☿	11	34	B
	☽✱♀	4pm	17	G
	☽∠♂	5	33	b
	☽P♃	8	9	G
	☽△♇	8	34	G
13	♅Stat	4am	13	
TU	☽☍♅	4	44	B
	☽△♄	6pm	24	G
	☽⊻♂	11	58	g
14	☽☍♃	5am	7	B
W	♀☍♇	9	45	
	☉P♅	10	14	
	☽□☉	10	55	B
15	☽⚼♄	1	1	b
TH	☽△☿	1	46	G
	☽P☿	2	47	G
	☽P♇	7	0	D
	☽□♇	8	52	B
	☽□♀	11	37	B
	☽P♂	0	20	B
16	☽⚼♆	6	0	b
F	☽⚼☿	9	37	b
	☽P♄	11	23	B
	☽☌♂	1pm	49	B
	☽⚼♅	11	43	b
17	☽△☉	5am	7	G
S	☽△♆	0pm	14	G
	☿⊥♀	0	48	
	♀△♅	6	31	
	☽✱♇	9	18	G
18	☽⚼♃	0am	38	b
SU	☽△♅	5	42	G
	☽△♀	6	58	G
	☽⚼☉	1pm	33	b
	☽P♄	4	39	B
	☿Q♃	4	41	
	☽☍♄	8	12	B
19	☽P♂	0am	30	B
M	☽⊻♂	2	36	g
	☽∠♇	2	46	b
	☉P♆	3	50	
	☽△♃	6	15	G
	☽⚼♀	3pm	28	b
	☽P♇	7	4	D
	☽□♆	10	57	B
20	☽P☿	4am	59	G
TU	☿⚻♇	7	0	

Date	Aspect	Time	Min	
	☽⚺♇	7	30	g
	☽☍☿	7	32	B
	☽∠♂	7	56	b
	☽□♅	3pm	34	B
	☿⚼♂	4	15	
	☉△♆	8	52	
21 W	☽✱♂	0	26	G
	☽□♃	3	6	B
	☽P♃	11	38	G
22 TH	☽✱♆	6am	34	G
	☽☍☉	9	13	B
	☽⚼♄	9	22	b
	☉∠♄	11	27	
	☽☌♇	2pm	36	D
	♀⚼♆	7	20	
	☽✱♅	10	20	G
23 F	☽∠♆	9am	19	b
	☽☍♀	10	43	B
	☽△♄	0pm	17	G
	☽□♂	7	16	B
	☽✱♃	9	0	G
	☽⚼☿	11	10	b
24 S	☽∠♅	0am	45	b
	♀✱♄	5	23	
	☽⚺♆	11	33	g
	☽⚺♇	7pm	12	g
	☿□♅	8	0	
	☽∠♃	11	9	b
25 SU	☽⚺♅	2am	44	g
	☽△☿	3	18	G
	☉☍♇	9	57	
	☽□♄	4pm	40	B
	☽∠♇	8	56	b
	☽⚼☉	9	46	b
26 M	☽△♂	0am	9	G
	☽⚺♃	0	59	g
	♂P♄	5	46	
	☽☌♆	2pm	59	D
	☽✱♇	10	28	G
	☽⚼♀	11	48	b
27 TU	☽△☉	1am	12	G
	☽P♃	2	2	G
	☽⚼♂	2	15	b
	☽☌♅	5	57	B
	☽□☿	11	0	B
	☽✱♄	8pm	7	G
	☽P☿	10	26	G
	♂⚻♃	11	17	
28 W	☽△♀	3am	42	G
	☽☌♃	4	10	G
	♀△♃	9	20	
	♀□♂	0pm	10	
	☽⚺♆	5	54	g
	☽∠♄	9	45	b
29 TH	☽□♇	1am	19	B
	☽P♇	1	21	D
	☽□☉	7	51	B
	☽⚺♅	8	51	g
	♂Q♇	10	40	
	☽✱☿	6pm	51	G
	☽∠♆	7	21	b
	♀⚼♅	10	3	
	☽P♄	10	4	B
	☉△♅	10	16	
	☽⚺♄	11	24	g
30 F	♀±♆	1am	47	
	☽P♂	1	52	B
	☽⚺♃	7	16	g
	☽☍♂	8	22	B
	☽∠♅	10	19	b
	☽□♀	11	30	B
	☽✱♆	8pm	51	G
	☽∠☿	11	1	b
31 S	☽△♇	4am	14	G
	☽∠♃	8	53	b
	☽✱♅	11	51	G
	☽✱☉	2pm	39	G
	☽P♂	6	55	B
	☿⚺♄	9	47	
JUNE				
1 SU	☽P♄	0am	35	B
	☽●♄	2	54	B
	☽⚺☿	3	26	g
	☽⚼♇	5	49	b
	☽✱♃	10	35	G
	☽∠☉	6pm	14	b
	☽✱♀	7	41	G
	☽P♇	9	4	D
2 M	☽□♆	0am	9	B
	☿P♃	5	51	
	☽⚼♂	3pm	18	b
	☽□♅	3	20	B
	♂⚼♅	4	46	
	☽⚺☉	10	4	g
3 TU	☽∠♀	0am	7	b
	☽⚺♄	7	1	g
	☽☌☿	1pm	23	G
	☽□♃	2	37	B
	☽△♂	6	7	G
	♀Q♄	8	3	
	☽P♃	8	59	G
	♀⚻♆	9	57	
4 W	☿□♃	0am	39	
	☽△♆	4	20	G
	☽⚺♀	4	58	g
	☽P☿	7	51	G
	☽∠♄	9	34	b
	☽☍♇	11	55	B
	☽△♅	7pm	57	G
5 TH	☿⊥♄	4am	37	
	☉⚼♆	6	52	
	☽⚼♆	7	3	b
	☽☌☉	7	4	D
	☽✱♄	0pm	36	G
	☿△♂	5	42	
	☽△♃	8	12	G
	☽⚼♅	11	0	b
6 F	☽□♂	1am	15	B
	☽⚺☿	2	5	g
	♀±♅	4	15	
	☽☌♀	4pm	44	G
	☽⚼♃	11	54	b
7 S	♀⚻♇	8am	24	
	☽∠☿	10	4	b
	☽P☿	5pm	39	G
	☽⚺☉	7	1	g
	☽□♄	8	41	B
	☽⚼♇	10	28	b
8 SU	☽✱♂	11am	23	G
	☿⊥♀	5pm	13	
	☿△♆	5	49	
	☉✱♄	6	51	
	☽☍♆	7	10	B
	☽✱☿	7	24	G
9 M	☽∠☉	2am	25	b
	☽△♇	3	27	G
	☽⚺♀	8	21	g
	☽P♃	9	47	G
	☽☍♅	0pm	24	B
	☿P♅	1	51	
	☽∠♂	5	43	b
	♀⚼♃	8	32	
10 TU	♃Stat	0am	25	
	☽△♄	7	48	G
	☽✱☉	10	44	G
	☽☍♃	3pm	27	B
	☽∠♀	5	37	b
	☿∠♄	5	58	
11 W	♀⚻♅	0am	7	
	☽⚺♂	0	45	g
	☿☍♇	2	4	
	☽⚼♄	2pm	16	b
	☿P♆	2	23	
	☽□♇	3	21	B
	☽P♇	5	10	D
	☽□☿	5	51	B
12 TH	☽✱♀	3am	29	G
	♀±♇	3	47	
	☽⚼♆	1pm	12	b
	☽P♄	3	2	B
	☉△♃	9	22	
13 F	☽□☉	4am	51	B
	☽⚼♅	7	1	b
	☿△♅	11	30	
	☽P♂	2pm	7	B
	☽●♂	3	45	B
	☽△♆	7	34	G
14 S	☽✱♇	4am	2	G
	☉⚼♅	7	4	
	☽P♂	7	54	B
	♂±♃	9	42	
	☽⚼♃	10	28	b
	☉±♆	0pm	24	
	☽△♅	1	11	G
	☽△☿	6	14	G
	☽□♀	10	57	B
15 SU	☽P♄	7am	50	B
	☽☍♄	9	31	B
	☽∠♇	9	49	b
	☽△♃	4pm	7	G
	☽△☉	9	49	G
16 M	☽P♇	4am	23	D
	☽⚺♂	5	16	g
	☽⚼☿	5	25	b
	☽□♆	6	47	B
	☿⚼♆	1pm	41	
	☽⚺♇	2	49	g
	♄⚼♇	9	47	
	☽□♅	11	29	B
17 TU	♀±♃	3am	53	
	☽⚼☉	4	50	b
	☿⚺♀	9	43	
	☽∠♂	10	42	b
	☽△♀	2pm	51	G
	♂△♆	11	33	
18 W	☽□♃	0am	50	B
	☽P♃	8	48	G
	☽✱♆	2pm	34	G
	☽✱♂	3	5	G
	☿✱♄	3	35	
	♀Q♂	4	15	
	☽⚼♀	8	56	b
	☽☌♇	10	4	D
	☽⚼♄	10	25	b
19 TH	☽✱♅	6am	10	G
	♀⚼♇	9	16	
	♀□♄	2pm	12	
	☽∠♆	5	6	b
	☉P♀	8	25	
	☿P♀	9	44	
	☉P☿	10	25	
20 F	☽△♄	0am	54	G
	☿△♃	1	45	
	☽✱♃	5	57	G
	☽☍☿	6	43	B
	☽∠♅	8	15	b
	☉⚻♆	3pm	58	
	☿⚼♅	4	32	
	☽⚺♆	6	56	g
	☽☍☉	7	9	B
	☿±♆	7	16	
	☽□♂	9	11	B
21 S	☽⚺♇	2am	2	g
	☽∠♃	7	28	b
	☽⚺♅	9	44	g
	♀⚻♃	11pm	11	
22 SU	☽∠♇	3am	13	b
	☽□♄	4	1	B
	☽⚺♃	8	32	g
	☽☍♀	9	26	B
	☉Q♄	9	44	
	☽☌♆	9pm	11	D
23 M	☽△♂	1am	3	G
	☉□♂	1	49	
	☽✱♇	4	7	G
	☽P♃	9	27	G
	☉±♅	11	12	
	☽☌♅	11	39	B
	☿⚻♆	0pm	49	
	☽⚼☿	11	40	b
24 TU	☽⚼♂	2am	44	b
	☽⚼☉	3	39	b
	☽✱♄	6	4	G
	☿Q♄	9	7	
	☽☌♃	10	11	G
	☿±♅	6pm	24	
	☽⚺♆	10	54	g
	☉⚻♇	10	55	
25 W	☿□♂	0am	26	
	☽△☿	5	5	G
	☽□♇	5	53	B
	☽△☉	6	23	G
	☽∠♄	7	8	b
	☽P♇	8	32	D
	☿⚻♇	10	16	
	☽⚺♅	1pm	26	g
	☽⚼♀	7	11	b
	☉☌☿	7	14	
	☽∠♆	11	57	b
26 TH	☽P♄	0am	55	B
	☽⚺♄	8	26	g
	☽⚺♃	0pm	14	g
	☽∠♅	2	38	b
	☿⚼♃	7	55	
	♂✱♇	9	9	
	☽△♀	10	52	G
	☽P♂	11	27	B
27 F	☽✱♆	1am	17	G
	☽△♇	8	25	G
	☽☍♂	8	49	B
	☿⚻♅	11	23	
	☽P♂	0pm	29	B
	☽□☉	0	42	B
	☽∠♃	1	40	b
	☽✱♅	4	7	G
	☽□☿	5	0	B
28 S	☉⚼♃	2am	3	
	♀☍♆	2	21	
	☿±♇	3	40	
	☽⚼♇	10	9	b
	☽P♄	11	4	B
	☽●♄	11	54	B
	☽✱♃	3pm	24	G
29 SU	☽P♇	3am	52	D
	☽□♆	4	54	B
	☽□♀	7	32	B
	☉⚻♅	1pm	26	
	☽□♅	8	7	B
	☽✱☉	8	38	G
30 M	☽✱☿	6am	57	G
	☽⚺♄	4pm	47	g
	☽⚼♂	6	6	b
	☽□♃	7	56	B
	☿±♃	9	39	
JULY				
1 TU	☽∠☉	1am	17	b
	☉±♇	2	34	
	☽P♃	7	44	G
	☽△♆	9	57	G
	♀△♇	11	47	
	☽∠☿	2pm	45	b
	☽☍♇	5	32	B
	☽✱♀	6	7	G
	☽∠♄	7	49	b
	☽△♂	10	4	G
2 W	☽△♅	1am	36	G
	☽⚺☉	6	27	g
	☿⚼♇	8	18	
	☽⚼♆	1pm	6	b
	♂⚼♃	2	29	
	☽⚺☿	11	12	g
	☽✱♄	11	17	G
	☿□♄	11	46	
3 TH	☽∠♀	0am	16	b
	☽△♃	2	2	G
	☽⚼♅	5	0	b
	☿⚻♃	4pm	44	
4 F	♄Q♅	5am	18	
	☽⚼♃	5	50	b
	☽⚺♀	7	7	g
	☽□♂	7	39	B
	♀✱♂	4pm	11	
	☽☌☉	6	40	D
	♀P♆	11	47	
5 S	♀☍♅	1am	40	
	☽⚼♇	5	0	b
	☽□♄	7	53	B
	♂△♅	2pm	17	
	☽☌☿	6	29	G
6 SU	☽☍♆	1am	45	B
	☿Q♂	2	22	
	☽△♇	10	0	G
	☉P☿	0pm	8	
	☽P♃	2	8	G
	☽☍♅	6	36	B
	☽✱♂	7	55	G
	☉±♃	9	14	
	☽☌♀	11	16	G
7 M	☽⚺☉	9am	55	g
	☿☍♆	4pm	4	
	☽△♄	6	55	G
	☽☍♃	8	44	B
	♀P♅	10	39	

Date	Aspect	Time		
8 TU	☽∠♂	3am	5	b
	☽⊻☿	5pm	14	g
	☽∠☉	6	38	b
	☽□♇	9	45	B
9 W	☽⚼♄	1am	15	b
	☽P♇	2	1	D
	☽⊻♂	10	48	g
	☽⊻♀	6pm	26	g
	☽⚼♆	7	31	b
	☽P♄	8	46	B
	☿△♇	9	39	
10 TH	☽⚹☉	3am	48	G
	☽∠☿	5	25	b
	☽P♂	6	48	B
	☉⚼♇	8	38	
	☽⚼♅	0pm	59	b
11 F	☽△♆	2am	0	G
	☽∠♀	4	28	b
	☽⚹♇	10	40	G
	☽⚼♃	3pm	18	b
	☽⚹☿	5	26	G
	☽△♅	7	20	G
12 S	☽☌♂	2am	32	B
	☿☍♅	5	55	
	☉□♄	7	48	
	☿P♆	9	16	
	☽P♂	1pm	42	B
	☽⚹♀	2	9	G
	☉⚻♃	3	23	
	☽∠♇	4	49	b
	☽P♄	8	27	B
	☽☍♄	8	40	B
	☽△♃	9	11	G
	☽□☉	9	44	B
13 SU	☽□♆	1	57	B
	☽P♇	2	38	D
	☽⊻♇	10	20	g
14 M	☿P♅	2am	56	
	☽□♅	6	31	B
	☽□☿	2pm	29	B
	☽⊻♂	4	7	g
	♃⚹♄	8	58	
15 TU	☽□♀	6am	36	B
	☽□♃	6	41	B
	♀☍♃	7	19	
	☿⚹♂	7	39	
	♀△♄	8	28	
	☽△☉	0pm	15	G
	☽∠♂	9	21	b
	☽⚹♆	10	41	G
16 W	☽P♃	2am	55	G
	☽P♀	6	9	G
	☽☌♇	6	33	D
	☽⚼♄	10	20	b
	☽⚹♅	2pm	4	G
	☽⚼☉	5	38	b
	♀P♃	10	9	
17 TH	☽⚹♂	1am	25	G
	☽P☿	1	27	G
	☽∠♆	1	33	b
	☽△☿	5	15	G
	♂P♄	7	14	
	☽⚹♃	0pm	16	G
	☽△♄	0	52	G
	☽∠♅	4	21	b
	☽△♀	5	45	G
18 F	☽⊻♆	3am	28	g
	☽⚼☿	10	22	b
	☽⊻♇	10	51	g

Date	Aspect	Time		
	☽∠♃	1pm	42	b
	☽⊻♅	5	47	g
	☽⚼♀	9	33	b
19 S	☽□♂	6am	35	B
	☽∠♇	11	50	b
	☽⊻♃	2pm	27	g
	☿☍♃	3	12	
	☽□♄	3	29	B
	☿P♃	6	39	
20 SU	☿△♄	1am	13	
	☽☍☉	3	20	B
	☽☌♆	5	12	D
	☽P♃	11	45	G
	☽⚹♇	0pm	19	G
	☽P☿	5	19	G
	☽☌♅	6	56	B
21 M	☽P♀	4am	1	G
	☉☍♆	7	15	
	☽△♂	9	21	G
	☽☌♃	2pm	49	G
	☽⚹♄	4	15	G
	☽☍☿	8	32	B
22 TU	☽☍♀	5am	24	B
	☽⊻♆	5	38	g
	♀⚻♆	8	12	
	☽⚼♂	10	31	b
	☽□♇	0pm	47	B
	☽P♇	4	32	D
	☽∠♄	4	32	b
	☽⊻♅	7	18	g
23 W	☽P♂	0am	28	B
	☽∠♆	5	56	b
	☉P♆	7	11	
	☽P♄	7	27	B
	☽⚼☉	9	16	b
	☽⊻♃	3pm	7	g
	☽⊻♄	5	1	g
	☽∠♅	7	43	b
24 TH	☽⚹♆	6am	32	G
	☽△☉	11	43	G
	☽△♇	1pm	56	G
	☽∠♃	3	43	b
	☽⚹♅	8	32	G
	♂∠♇	9	20	
25 F	☽⚼☿	6am	16	b
	☽⚼♀	2pm	22	b
	☽⚼♇	3	9	b
	☽☍♂	3	55	B
	☽⚹♃	4	48	G
	☽●♄	7	14	B
	☽P♄	7	20	B
	☿⚻♆	8	2	
	☉△♇	8	40	
	♀□♇	11	27	
26 S	☽P♂	7am	8	B
	☽□♆	9	10	B
	♂△♃	10	16	
	☉⊻☿	10	20	
	☽△☿	10	34	G
	☽P♇	11	16	D
	☽□☉	6pm	28	B
	☽△♀	6	38	G
	♀∠♂	11	4	
	☽□♅	11	45	B
27 SU	♀±♆	5am	10	
	☉P♅	5	39	
	☽P♀	6	23	G
	☽P☿	6	35	G
	☿P♀	0pm	13	

Date	Aspect	Time		
	☽□♃	8	37	B
	☽⊻♄	11	41	g
	♀⚼♄	11	47	
28 M	☽△♆	2	7	G
	☽□☿	9	16	B
	☽☍♇	10	20	B
29 TU	☽P♃	1am	26	G
	☽⚼♂	2	47	b
	☽∠♄	2	48	b
	♀⚻♅	3	22	
	♂☍♄	3	25	
	☽⚹☉	4	9	G
	☽△♅	5	19	G
	☽□♀	5	31	B
	♂P♇	8	11	
	☿□♇	8	47	
	☽⚼♆	5pm	30	b
	☉☍♅	7	29	
30 W	☽△♃	2am	47	G
	☽⚹♄	6	31	G
	☽△♂	7	47	G
	☽⚼♅	8	59	b
	☽∠☉	10	7	b
	☿±♆	2pm	9	
	☽P☉	10	8	G
31 TH	☽⚼♃	6am	42	b
	☽⚹☿	10	39	G
	☿P♂	10	51	
	☿⚼♄	0pm	23	
	☽⊻☉	4	48	g
	☽⚹♀	7	33	G

AUGUST

Date	Aspect	Time		
1 F	☽P☉	2am	3	G
	♀P♂	2	45	
	☿P♇	6	37	
	☽⚼♇	10	48	b
	☿⚻♅	3pm	33	
	☽□♄	3	38	B
	♄Stat	4	56	
	☽∠☿	6	14	b
	☽□♂	7	46	B
2 S	☽∠♀	3am	41	b
	☽☍♆	7	1	B
	☽P♃	9	2	G
	♀P♇	9	22	
	☽△♇	4pm	4	G
	☽☍♅	11	19	B
	♀±♅	11	26	
3 SU	☽⊻☿	2am	21	g
	☽☌☉	8	14	D
	☿∠♂	0pm	3	
	☽⊻♀	0	30	g
	♀⚼♆	1	7	
	☽☍♃	9	36	B
4 M	☽△♄	2am	50	G
	☉Q♂	6	23	
	☽⚹♂	10	11	G
	♀±♄	11	57	
	☽P♂	9pm	51	B
5 TU	☽□♇	4am	0	B
	☽P♇	8	39	D
	☽⚼♄	9	5	b
	☽∠♂	6pm	7	b
	☽●☿	7	44	G
	☽P♀	8	44	G
6 W	☽⚼♆	0am	56	b
	☽⊻☉	1	58	g
	☽P☿	2	47	G

Date	Aspect	Time		
	☽P♄	4	12	B
	☽☌♀	7	51	G
	☿P♄	1pm	5	
	☉P♃	5	23	
	☽⚼♅	5	42	b
	♀⚻♃	11	43	
7 TH	☽⊻♂	2am	18	g
	☽△♆	7	26	G
	☽∠☉	11	15	b
	☽⚼♃	3pm	52	b
	☽⚹♇	5	4	G
	☿±♅	11	59	
8 F	☽△♅	0am	10	G
	♀P♄	2	17	
	☽⊻☿	1pm	9	g
	☽⚹☉	8	24	G
	☽P☿	9	38	G
	☽△♃	9	58	G
	☽∠♇	11	28	b
9 S	☿⚼♆	1am	8	
	☽P♀	1	34	G
	♂⊥♇	3	41	
	☽⊻♀	3	42	g
	☽☍♄	4	28	B
	☽P♄	4	45	B
	♀⚻♄	11	22	
	☉☍♃	1pm	40	
	☽☌♂	6	16	B
	☽□♆	7	58	B
	☽∠☿	9	4	b
	♀Q♇	9	51	
10 SU	☽P♇	0am	29	D
	☽⊻♇	5	26	g
	♀⚼♅	6	8	
	☽□♅	0pm	9	B
	☽∠♀	0	49	b
	♀⊥♂	4	29	
	☽P♂	9	15	B
11 M	☿±♄	0am	48	
	♂□♆	2	50	
	☽⚹☿	4	0	G
	☽□♃	8	39	B
	♀±♃	0pm	21	
	☽□☉	0	42	B
	☽⚹♀	8	53	G
12 TU	☽P☉	5am	42	G
	☽⚹♆	5	59	G
	☽⊻♂	7	24	g
	☽☌♇	3pm	1	D
	☽⚼♄	7	30	b
	☽⚹♅	9	8	G
	☉△♄	11	0	
13 W	☽P♃	3am	41	G
	♇Stat	8	39	
	☽∠♆	9	34	b
	☽∠♂	0pm	18	b
	☽□☿	2	3	B
	☽⚹♃	3	52	G
	☿P♀	9	23	
	☽△♄	10	35	G
14 TH	☽∠♅	0am	7	b
	☽△☉	0	25	G
	☽□♀	9	1	B
	☽⊻♆	0pm	7	g
	☽⚹♂	4	2	G
	☽∠♃	6	0	b
	☽⊻♇	8	35	g
15 F	☽⊻♅	2am	7	g
	☽⚼☉	4	23	b

Date	Aspect	Time		
	☽△☿	6pm	58	G
	☽⊻♃	7	13	g
	♀△♆	8	13	
	☽∠♇	9	57	b
16 S	☽□♄	1am	51	B
	☿∠♂	3	48	
	☿⚻♃	7	11	
	☽P♃	9	18	G
	☽☌♆	2pm	31	D
	☽△♀	4	10	G
	☽⚼☿	7	54	b
	☽□♂	8	28	B
	☽⚹♇	10	34	G
17 SU	☽☌♅	3am	40	B
	☽⚼♀	6pm	28	b
	☽☌♃	7	38	G
	☿Stat	7	48	
	☽P☉	7	59	G
	☽P♂	10	36	B
18 M	☽⚹♄	2am	20	G
	♀⚼♃	8	1	
	☽☍☉	10	55	B
	☉P♂	1pm	11	
	☽⊻♆	2	35	g
	☽△♂	10	30	G
	☽□♇	10	30	B
	♂⊻♇	10	40	
19 TU	☽P♇	1am	34	D
	☽∠♄	2	6	b
	☽⊻♅	3	22	g
	☽∠♆	2pm	20	b
	☽P♄	6	18	B
	☽⊻♃	6	53	g
	☽☍☿	7	28	B
	☽⚼♂	11	20	b
	♀⚹♇	11	54	
20 W	☽⊻♄	1am	52	g
	☽∠♅	3	8	b
	☽P☿	2pm	10	G
	☽⚹♆	2	12	G
	☽P♀	5	28	G
	☽∠♃	6	39	b
	☉⊥♀	6	40	
	☉⚻♆	7	13	
	☽△♇	10	19	G
21 TH	☽☍♀	0am	15	B
	☽⚹♅	3	9	G
	♀⊻♂	3	56	
	☽P♀	3	58	G
	☽P☿	6	12	G
	☽⚼☉	3pm	48	b
	☽⚹♃	6	47	G
	☽⚼♇	10	45	b
22 F	☿⚻♃	0am	3	
	☽●♄	2	18	B
	☽P♄	2	20	B
	☿P♀	2	32	
	♀△♅	11	34	
	☽□♆	3pm	11	B
	☽△☉	6	25	G
	☽⚼☿	7	4	b
	☽P♇	8	24	D
23 S	☽☍♂	4am	14	B
	☽□♅	4	42	B
	♂□♅	1pm	53	
	☽P☉	2	14	G
	☽△☿	7	44	G
	☽□♃	8	51	B
24	☽⊻♄	5am	8	g

SU	☽⚼♀	10	43	b
	☽P♂	1pm	41	B
	☽△♆	6	50	G
	☿±♄	8	8	
25	☽□☉	2am	24	B
M	☽☍♇	4	4	B
	☽∠♄	7	43	b
	☽△♅	9	9	G
	☽△♀	4pm	12	G
	☽⚼♆	9	53	b
	☽□☿	10	43	B
26	☽P♃	1am	2	G
TU	☉□♇	1	48	
	☽△♃	2	0	G
	♃Q♇	10	20	
	☽⚹♄	11	7	G
	☽⚼♅	0pm	37	b
	☿⚼♆	1	27	
	☽⚼♂	4	29	b
	☉±♆	9	20	
27	☽⚼♃	5am	45	b
W	☿⚺♀	2pm	8	
	☽⚹☉	2	26	G
	☿±♅	8	22	
	☽△♂	10	26	G
28	☉⚼♄	1am	9	
TH	☽⚹☿	3	50	G
	☽□♀	6	19	B
	☽⚼♇	4pm	33	b
	☽□♄	8	9	B
	☉▽♅	8	48	
	☽P♃	9	11	G
	☽∠☉	9	51	b
29	♀P♄	3am	25	
F	☽∠☿	7	4	b
	☽☍♆	11	35	B
	♀△♃	8pm	16	
	☿⚹♂	8	59	
	☽△♇	10	4	G
30	☽P♂	0am	52	B
S	☽☍♅	3	16	B
	☽⚺☉	6	1	g
	☽⚺☿	10	40	g
	☿⊥♀	11	14	
	☽□♂	0pm	34	B
	☽☍♃	8	56	B
	☽⚹♀	11	53	G
31	☉P♇	6am	57	
SU	☽△♄	7	30	G
	☉☌☿	1pm	43	
SEPTEMBER				
1	☿P♄	7am	23	
M	☽∠♀	9	29	b
	☽□♇	10	23	B
	☽P♇	1pm	13	D
	☽⚼♄	1	43	b
	☽P☉	5	1	G
	♀∠♇	6	37	
	☽☌☿	6	48	G
	☽P♀	11	26	G
	☽•●	11	52	D
2	☽⚹♂	4am	41	G
TU	☽⚼♆	5	55	b
	☽P☿	9	14	G
	☽P♄	1pm	23	B
	☽⚺♀	7	22	g
	☉P♀	9	50	
	☽⚼♅	9	57	b
3	♀☍♄	2am	26	
W	☽△♆	0pm	25	G
	☽∠♂	1	2	b
	☽⚼♃	3	24	b
	☿▽♅	6	43	
	☿∠♀	7	55	
	☉±♅	8	56	
	☽⚹♇	11	31	G
4	☽⚺☿	3am	51	g
TH	☽△♅	4	25	G
	☉P☿	4pm	17	
	☽⚺☉	6	23	g
	☽⚺♂	9	19	g
	☽△♃	9	37	G
	♀P♇	9	58	
5	☉⚼♆	0am	17	
F	♂□♃	2	5	
	☿⚼♄	4	24	
	☽∠♇	5	59	b
	☽P♄	8	21	B
	☽∠☿	8	35	b
	☽☍♄	8	48	B
	☽☌♀	3pm	0	G
	☽P☉	6	34	G
	☉±♄	9	24	
6	☽□♆	1am	5	B
S	☽P☿	2	23	G
	☽∠☉	3	19	b
	☉▽♃	6	33	
	☽P♇	9	5	D
	☽⚺♇	0pm	7	g
	☽⚹☿	1	20	G
	☽P♀	3	7	G
	☽□♅	4	43	B
	☿±♆	8	19	
7	☿Q♂	6am	40	
SU	☽□♃	9	8	B
	☽⚹☉	11	39	G
	☽☌♂	0pm	44	B
	♂Q♆	0	57	
8	☿□♇	0am	37	
M	☿P♇	6	24	
	☽⚺♀	8	33	g
	☽⚹♆	11	59	G
	☽□☿	10pm	14	B
	☽☌♇	10	40	D
9	☽⚼♄	0am	49	b
TU	☽⚹♅	2	51	G
	☉⚹♂	4	27	
	♀⊥♇	1pm	8	
	☽∠♀	3	51	b
	☽∠♆	4	18	b
	☽⚹♃	6	7	G
	♂P♃	7	58	
	♀□♆	8	52	
10	☽⚺♂	1am	0	g
W	☽□☉	1	31	B
	☿Stat	1	42	
	☉P♄	2	42	
	☽△♄	4	38	G
	☽P♃	6	13	G
	☽∠♅	6	41	b
	☽P♂	8	44	B
	☽⚺♆	7pm	43	g
	☽∠♃	9	20	b
	☽⚹♀	9	56	G
11	☽△☿	5am	22	G
TH	☽∠♂	5	33	b
	☽⚺♇	5	50	g
	☽⚺♅	9	34	g
	☽P♂	4pm	44	B
	☉▽♄	5	9	
	☉±♃	10	20	
	☽⚺♃	11	36	g
12	☽P♃	3am	0	G
F	☿□♇	7	0	
	☽∠♇	8	0	b
	☽⚼☿	8	2	b
	☽⚹♂	9	1	G
	☽□♄	9	30	B
	☽△☉	10	48	G
	♂▽♄	6pm	22	
	☉⚼♅	9	18	
	☽☌♆	11	45	D
13	☿±♆	0am	35	
S	☽□♀	6	26	B
	☽⚹♇	9	19	G
	☽☌♅	0pm	40	B
	☽⚼☉	1	48	b
	☉Q♇	9	7	
	☿⚼♄	11	16	
14	☽☌♃	1am	40	G
SU	☽P♀	7	2	G
	☽⚹♄	11	3	G
	☽□♂	1pm	10	B
	♀⚺♇	6	43	
15	☽⚺♆	0am	44	g
M	☽P☿	3	49	G
	☽□♇	9	58	B
	☽∠♄	10	58	b
	☽P♇	10	59	D
	☽△♀	11	13	G
	☽☍☿	0pm	51	B
	☽⚺♅	1	3	g
	☿▽♅	4	32	
16	☽∠♆	0am	32	b
TU	☽⚺♃	1	26	g
	☽P♄	8	26	B
	☽⚺♄	10	35	g
	♀□♅	10	50	
	☽∠♅	0pm	44	b
	☽⚼♀	0	53	b
	☽△♂	3	4	G
	☽☍☉	6	50	B
	☽P☉	8	48	G
17	☽⚹♆	0am	10	G
W	☽∠♃	0	59	b
	☽△♇	9	25	G
	☽⚹♅	0pm	22	G
	☽⚼♂	3	51	b
	☽P☉	6	59	G
18	☽⚹♃	0am	37	G
TH	☽P♄	9	1	B
	☽⚼♇	9	17	b
	☽•♄	9	53	B
	☽⚼☿	5pm	16	b
	♂Q♅	6	57	
	☽□♆	11	57	B
19	☽P♇	7am	32	D
F	☽P☿	9	58	G
	☽□♅	0pm	31	B
	♂P♅	6	7	
	☽☍♀	6	58	B
	☽△☿	8	2	G
20	☽⚼☉	0am	14	b
S	☽□♃	1	9	B
	☉△♆	5	6	
	☽⚺♄	10	50	g
	☉⚼♃	1pm	9	
	☿P♇	1	9	
	♂±♄	7	30	
	☽☍♂	9	3	B
	☿±♅	9	8	
21	☽△♆	1am	56	G
SU	☽△☉	3	31	G
	☽☍♇	0pm	17	B
	☽∠♄	0	27	b
	☽△♅	3	16	G
	☿⚼♆	6	52	
	☿±♄	7	43	
	☽P♀	8	8	G
	☿▽♃	11	10	
22	☽⚼♆	4am	12	b
M	☽△♃	4	39	G
	☽□☿	5	22	B
	♄⚼♇	10	56	
	☽⚹♄	2pm	59	G
	☽⚼♅	6	1	b
	☿Q♂	6	6	
	♀□♃	9	29	
23	☽P♃	0am	51	G
TU	☽⚼♃	7	50	b
	☽⚼♀	8	53	b
	☽□☉	1pm	35	B
	♂P♆	3	27	
24	☽P♃	10am	42	G
W	☽⚼♂	11	0	b
	☽△♀	4pm	1	G
	☽P♀	8	3	G
	☽⚹☿	9	1	G
	♂⚹♆	10	52	
	☽□♄	10	55	B
	☽⚼♇	11	22	b
25	♀Q♆	7am	11	
TH	☿▽♄	10	35	
	☿±♃	2pm	56	
	♀P♃	3	33	
	☽☍♆	4	45	B
	☽△♂	5	50	G
26	☽⚹☉	4am	23	G
F	☽△♇	4	51	G
	☽∠☿	7	7	b
	☽☍♅	7	52	B
	☉⚹♇	10	12	
	☿⚼♅	0pm	20	
	☽☍♃	10	42	B
27	☿Q♇	9am	20	
S	☽□♀	9	24	B
	☽△♄	9	58	G
	☽∠☉	1pm	6	b
	♀▽♄	2	57	
	☽⚺☿	6	18	g
	☉△♅	10	40	
28	☿P♄	9am	23	
SU	☽□♂	9	43	B
	☽⚼♄	4pm	10	b
	☽P♇	5	4	D
	☽□♇	5	24	B
	☽⚺☉	10	17	g
29	♂Q♃	6am	7	
M	☽⚼♆	11	18	b
	♀P♅	10pm	0	
30	☽P♄	0am	24	B
TU	☽⚼♅	2	49	b
	☽⚹♀	4	51	G
	☽P☿	9	24	G
	☽P☉	10	20	G
	☉P☿	0pm	47	
	☿⚼♃	4	3	
	☿△♆	4	13	
	☽⚼♃	5	49	b
	☽△♆	5	51	G
	☽☌☿	6	8	G
OCTOBER				
1	☽⚹♂	2am	38	G
W	☽⚹♇	6	36	G
	☽△♅	9	18	G
	☽∠♀	2pm	34	b
	☽☌☉	4	52	D
	♀P♆	5	42	
	☽P☿	6	12	G
	♀Q♅	10	50	
2	☽△♃	0am	10	G
TH	☽P☉	4	11	G
	☽P♄	9	9	B
	☽∠♂	10	52	b
	☽☍♄	10	58	B
	♂⚼♄	0pm	21	
	☽∠♇	0	58	b
	♀±♄	1	47	
	☽⚺♀	11	57	g
3	☽□♆	6am	21	B
F	☽P♇	4pm	48	D
	☽⚺☿	5	16	g
	☽⚺♂	6	43	g
	☽⚺♇	7	0	g
	☽□♅	9	27	B
	♂☌♇	11	44	
4	☉P♄	0am	7	
S	☿⚹♇	5	3	
	☿⚹♂	8	22	
	☽⚺☉	10	10	g
	☽□♃	11	56	B
	☿△♅	9pm	21	
5	☽∠☿	3am	52	b
SU	☉△♃	7	42	
	☽☌♀	5pm	1	G
	♂⚹♅	5	8	
	☽⚹♆	5	17	G
	☽∠☉	5	57	b
	♀⚹♆	8	6	
6	☽⚼♄	2am	59	b
M	☽☌♇	5	38	D
	☽⚹♅	7	50	G
	☽☌♂	8	44	B
	☽⚹☿	1pm	34	G
	☽⚹♃	9	45	G
	☽∠♆	9	55	b
7	☽⚹☉	0am	59	G
TU	☽△♄	7	14	G
	☽∠♅	0pm	8	b
	☽P♃	8	49	G
8	☽∠♃	1am	43	b
W	☽⚺♆	1	53	g
	♃Stat	4	38	
	☽⚺♀	6	56	g
	♀Q♃	10	24	
	♀P♂	0pm	11	
	☽⚺♇	1	46	g
	☽⚺♅	3	43	g
	☽⚺♂	7	45	g
9	☿△♃	0am	1	
TH	♆Stat	1	29	
	☉∠♀	2	16	
	☽P♃	3	47	G

	☽⚺♃	4	58	g
	☽□☿	5	43	B
	☽□☉	0pm	22	B
	☽∠♀	0	28	b
	☽□♄	1	38	B
	☽∠♇	4	44	b
	☿P♄	7	49	
	☽∠♂	11	58	b
10	♀⚼♄	1am	40	
F	☉☍♄	4	26	
	☽☌♆	7	35	D
	☽✱♀	5pm	1	G
	☽✱♇	6	56	G
	☽☌♅	8	39	B
11	☽✱♂	3am	17	G
S	☽☌♃	9	11	G
	☿☍♄	4pm	28	
	☽✱♄	5	4	G
	☽△☿	5	9	G
	♀☌♇	5	41	
	☽△☉	8	0	G
12	☉∠♇	1am	53	
SU	♄Q♅	7	49	
	☽⚺♆	10	21	g
	♀✱♅	2pm	40	
	☽∠♄	5	47	b
	☽P♇	7	36	D
	☿∠♇	8	28	
	☽□♇	9	13	B
	☽⚼☿	9	19	b
	☽⚼☉	10	34	b
	☽⚺♅	10	45	g
	☽□♀	11	24	B
13	☽P☉	3am	11	G
M	☽□♂	7	37	B
	☽P☿	8	44	G
	☽⚺♃	10	46	g
	☽∠♆	10	50	b
	☽⚺♄	6pm	0	g
	☉☌☿	9	2	
	☽∠♅	11	0	b
	☽P♄	11	34	B
14	♅Stat	10am	49	
TU	☽∠♃	10	53	b
	☽✱♆	10	56	G
	☿∠♀	7pm	59	
	☽△♇	9	35	G
	☽✱♅	10	58	G
15	☽△♀	3am	24	G
W	☽△♂	10	3	G
	☽✱♃	10	48	G
	☽P♄	3pm	47	B
	☽•♄	5	38	B
	☽⚼♇	9	30	b
16	♂∠♆	2am	12	
TH	♂✱♃	2	16	
	☽☍☉	3	46	B
	☽⚼♀	5	11	b
	☽☍☿	6	39	B
	☉P☿	9	32	
	☽□♆	10	46	B
	☽⚼♂	11	12	b
	☿P♇	2pm	24	
	☉P♇	7	8	
	☽P♇	7	58	D
	☽P☉	8	2	G
	☽P☿	9	7	G
	☽□♅	10	54	B
17	☽□♃	11am	3	B

F	☽⚺♄	5pm	43	g
	☿□♆	7	34	
18	☿⊥♇	6am	43	
S	☽△♆	11	45	G
	☽∠♄	6pm	31	b
	☽☍♇	11	11	B
19	☽△♅	0am	28	G
SU	☿∠♂	3	29	
	♀∠♆	10	19	
	☽⚼☉	11	22	b
	♀✱♃	0pm	24	
	☽⚼♆	1	16	b
	☽△♃	1	26	G
	☽☍♀	1	31	B
	☽☍♂	5	50	B
	☽⚼☿	6	55	b
	☽✱♄	8	7	G
20	☽⚼♅	2am	26	b
M	☽P♃	6	20	G
	☉□♆	2pm	7	
	☽△☉	3	52	G
	☽⚼♃	3	58	b
21	☽△☿	1am	22	G
TU	♂△♄	9	9	
	☉⊥♇	10	54	
	☽P♃	11pm	16	G
22	☿⚺♇	0am	21	
W	☽□♄	2	17	B
	☽⚼♇	8	13	b
	☿□♅	10	14	
	♀△♄	8pm	51	
	☽☍♆	11	48	B
23	☽□☉	4am	48	B
TH	☽⚼♀	7	55	b
	☽⚼♂	10	5	b
	☽△♇	1pm	16	G
	☽☍♅	2	30	B
	☽□☿	6	46	B
24	☽P☿	4am	36	G
F	☽☍♃	5	49	B
	☽△♄	0pm	21	G
	☽△♀	4	30	G
	☽△♂	5	45	G
25	☽P☉	0am	1	G
S	☽⚼♄	6pm	25	b
	☽P♇	10	2	D
	☽✱☉	10	7	G
26	☽□♇	1am	36	B
SU	♀☌♂	11	34	
	♀∠♅	0pm	12	
	♂∠♅	0	29	
	☽✱☿	4	32	G
	☽⚼♆	5	58	b
27	☽∠☉	7am	31	b
M	☽⚼♅	9	20	b
	☿□♃	9	46	
	☽□♂	10	42	B
	☽□♀	11	24	B
	☽P♄	0pm	40	B
	☉⚺♇	4	33	
	♀⊥♆	9	53	
28	☽△♆	0am	33	G
TU	☽⚼♃	1	29	b
	☽∠☿	3	48	b
	☉□♅	5	11	
	♂⊥♆	0pm	55	
	☽✱♇	2	51	G
	☽△♅	3	52	G
	☽⚺☉	4	50	g

29	☿Q♆	1am	34	
W	☿⚻♄	4	7	
	☽△♃	8	0	G
	☽P♄	10	35	B
	☿⊥♂	0pm	51	
	☽☍♄	1	15	B
	☽⚺☿	2	40	g
	☽∠♇	9	8	b
30	☽✱♂	3am	19	G
TH	☽✱♀	5	48	G
	☿P♃	9	44	
	☽□♆	0pm	56	B
31	☽P♇	0am	59	D
F	☽⚺♇	2	57	g
	☽□♅	3	49	B
	☽☌☉	10	1	D
	☿⊥♀	10	18	
	☽∠♂	10	51	b
	☽∠♀	2pm	7	b
	☽□♃	7	45	B

NOVEMBER

1	☽☌☿	10am	13	G
S	☽⚺♂	5pm	45	g
	☽P☉	8	36	G
	☿±♄	9	27	
	☽⚺♀	9	43	g
	☉∠♂	11	12	
	☽✱♆	11	22	G
2	☽⚼♄	4am	47	b
SU	☽☌♇	0pm	59	D
	☽✱♅	1	44	G
	♀⚺♆	6	13	
	☿P♅	9	42	
3	☿Q♅	0am	16	
M	☽⚺☉	0	32	g
	☽∠♆	3	47	b
	☽✱♃	5	21	G
	☽△♄	8	55	G
	☽P♃	0pm	51	G
	♀∠♃	2	52	
	☽∠♅	5	53	b
4	☽⚺☿	2am	29	g
TU	☽☌♂	5	38	B
	☽∠☉	6	47	b
	♀⊥♅	7	14	
	☿P♆	7	20	
	☽⚺♆	7	41	g
	☽∠♃	9	23	b
	☽☌♀	10	48	G
	☽⚺♇	8pm	54	g
	☽⚺♅	9	32	g
5	☽∠☿	9am	28	b
W	☽✱☉	0pm	24	G
	☽⚺♃	0	53	g
	☽□♄	3	42	B
	♂⚺♆	6	7	
	☉□♃	7	27	
	☿✱♆	11	49	
6	☽∠♇	0am	6	b
TH	☽P♃	0	24	G
	☿⚺♂	5	23	
	☽☌♆	1pm	58	D
	☽⚺♂	3	6	g
	☽✱☿	3	42	G
	☽⚺♀	9	15	g
	☽P☉	9	23	G
7	☽✱♇	2am	47	G
F	☽☌♅	3	19	B

	☉⚻♄	5	37	
	♂∠♃	7	29	
	☿⚼♄	2pm	52	
	☽☌♃	6	24	G
	☽∠♂	6	56	b
	☉Q♆	7	26	
	☽✱♄	8	29	G
	♂⊥♅	9	16	
	☽□☉	9	43	B
8	☽∠♀	1am	29	b
S	☽⚺♆	6pm	13	g
	☿Q♃	9	29	
	☽∠♄	10	8	b
	☽✱♂	10	11	G
9	☽□☿	1am	57	B
SU	☽P♇	2	33	D
	☽✱♀	5	4	G
	☽□♇	6	38	B
	☽⚺♅	7	5	g
	☽∠♆	7pm	36	b
	☽⚺♃	9	53	g
	☽⚺♄	11	19	g
10	☽△☉	4am	33	G
M	♀⚺♇	4	39	
	☽∠♅	8	15	b
	♀⚺♅	11	0	
	☽P♄	0pm	46	B
	☽✱♆	8	34	G
	☽∠♃	10	57	b
11	☿☌♇	0am	17	
TU	☽□♂	3	4	B
	☿✱♅	4	18	
	☽⚼☉	7	11	b
	☽△♇	8	40	G
	☽✱♅	9	3	G
	☽△☿	9	34	G
	☽□♀	10	35	B
	☉P♃	0pm	36	
	☽P♄	10	32	B
	☽✱♃	11	44	G
12	☽•♄	0am	35	B
W	☽⚼♇	9	15	b
	☽⚼☿	0pm	45	b
	☿⚺♀	1	53	
	☉±♄	8	59	
	☽□♆	9	42	B
13	☽△♂	6am	43	G
TH	☽P♇	8	13	D
	☽□♅	10	6	B
	☽△♀	2pm	57	G
	♀⊥♃	6	38	
14	☽□♃	1am	3	B
F	☽⚺♄	1	22	g
	☽⚼♂	8	37	b
	☽☍☉	2pm	12	B
	☽⚼♀	5	18	b
	☽△♆	11	0	G
15	☽∠♄	2am	4	b
S	♃✱♄	3	53	
	☽☍♇	11	27	B
	☽△♅	11	45	G
	☉Q♅	0pm	18	
	♂⚺♇	8	44	
	☽☍☿	11	10	B
16	☽⚼♆	0am	17	b
SU	☽P♃	1	1	G
	♂⚺♅	2	27	
	☽✱♄	3	18	G
	☽△♃	3	35	G

	☿P♂	7	42	
	☿∠♆	10	31	
	☽⚼♅	1pm	23	b
	♀⊥♇	6	52	
17	☽⚼♃	5am	54	b
M	☿△♄	3pm	29	
	☽☍♂	6	1	B
	☿✱♃	11	35	
18	☽⚼☉	1am	49	b
TU	☽☍♀	4	41	B
	☽□♄	8	10	B
	☽⚼♇	7pm	2	b
19	☽P♃	3am	37	G
W	☽△☉	7	59	G
	☽☍♆	9	10	B
	☉P♅	1pm	12	
	☽⚼☿	5	41	b
	☉✱♆	11	14	
	☽△♇	11	32	G
	☽☍♅	11	47	B
20	♀□♄	5am	22	
TH	☽△♄	4pm	57	G
	☽☍♃	6	51	B
21	☽△☿	2am	27	G
F	♂⊥♃	7	48	
	☉⚼♄	9	15	
	♀⚺♃	9	19	
	☽⚼♂	1pm	11	b
	☽⚼♄	10	40	b
	☽□☉	11	58	B
22	☽⚼♀	2am	6	b
S	☿∠♅	4	39	
	☽P♇	5	10	D
	☽□♇	11	10	B
	☉P♆	5pm	50	
	☽△♂	9	30	G
23	☽⚼♆	2am	20	b
SU	☿⊥♆	6	28	
	☽△♀	10	54	G
	☿P♀	11	32	
	☽⚼♅	5pm	58	b
	☽□☿	10	21	B
24	☽P♄	0am	45	B
M	♂⊥♇	4	0	
	☽△♆	8	57	G
	☽⚼♃	2pm	44	b
	☽✱☉	6	37	G
25	☽✱♇	0am	23	G
TU	☽△♅	0	35	G
	☽□♂	2pm	41	B
	☽P♄	3	36	B
	☽☍♄	5	40	B
	☽△♃	9	26	G
26	☉Q♃	1am	16	
W	☽∠☉	3	42	b
	☽□♀	4	17	B
	☽∠♇	6	42	b
	☽✱☿	5pm	36	G
	☽□♆	9	26	B
27	☽P♇	10am	41	D
TH	☉∠♀	11	1	
	♂□♄	11	5	
	☽⚺☉	0pm	5	g
	☽⚺♇	0	26	g
	☽□♅	0	36	B
	☉☌♇	4	34	
	♀∠♇	6	11	
	☉✱♅	6	34	
28	☽∠☿	1am	51	b

Date	Aspect	h	m	
F	☽✱♂	5	54	G
	☽□♃	9	10	B
	☿⊻♆	1pm	35	
	☽✱♀	6	58	G
29	☽✱♆	7am	30	G
S	☽⊻☿	9	0	g
	☽⚼♄	9	13	b
	☽∠♂	0pm	17	b
	☽☌♇	9	52	D
	☽✱♅	10	1	G
30	☽∠♀	1am	0	b
SU	☽☌☉	2	14	D
	☽P♃	2	45	G
	☿⊥♅	9	43	
	☽∠♆	11	31	b
	☽△♄	1pm	4	G
	☽⊻♂	5	53	g
	☽✱♃	6	7	G
	♂⊻♃	10	47	
DECEMBER				
1	☽∠♅	1am	44	b
M	☽⊻♀	6	14	g
	☽⊻♆	2pm	57	g
	☽☌☿	8	11	G
	☽∠♃	9	41	b
2	☽⊻♇	4am	47	g
TU	☽⊻♅	4	55	g
	☽⊻☉	1pm	17	g
	☽□♄	7	10	B
3	☽⊻♃	0am	48	g
W	☽☌♂	3	12	B
	☽∠♇	7	34	b
	☿∠♃	8	31	
	☽☌♀	2pm	52	G
	☽∠☉	6	1	b
	☽☌♆	8	29	D
4	☽P♃	0am	52	G
TH	☽⊻☿	4	9	g
	☽✱♇	10	0	G
	☽☌♅	10	8	B
	☽✱☉	10pm	21	G
	☽✱♄	11	49	G
5	☉∠♆	4am	6	
F	☽☌♃	6	2	G
	☽∠☿	7	12	b

Date	Aspect	h	m	
	☽⊻♂	10	53	g
	☉△♄	5pm	53	
	☽⊻♀	9	52	g
6	☽⊻♆	0am	49	g
S	☽∠♄	1	46	b
	☽P♇	8	17	D
	☽✱☿	9	41	G
	♂∠♇	11	24	
	☽□♇	2pm	8	B
	☽⊻♅	2	16	g
	☽∠♂	2	17	b
7	☽∠♀	0am	53	b
SU	☽∠♆	2	38	b
	☽⊻♄	3	29	g
	☽□☉	6	9	B
	☽⊻♃	10	17	g
	☽∠♅	4pm	0	b
	☿Stat	4	55	
	☽✱♂	5	26	G
	☽P♄	9	59	B
8	☽✱♀	3am	37	G
M	☽✱♆	4	15	G
	☉⊥♂	7	2	
	♀P♂	8	12	
	☽∠♃	0pm	6	b
	☽□☿	1	0	B
	☉P♀	3	16	
	☽△♇	5	24	G
	☽✱♅	5	32	G
	☉P♂	6	18	
	♀☌♆	7	31	
9	☽P♄	5am	22	B
TU	☽☌♄	6	22	B
	♃Q♇	10	15	
	☽△☉	0pm	57	G
	☽✱♃	1	44	G
	☿∠♃	6	22	
	☽⚼♇	6	46	b
	☽□♂	11	6	B
10	☉✱♃	2am	0	
W	☽□♆	6	59	B
	☽□♀	8	22	B
	☽△☿	2pm	23	G
	☽⚼☉	4	7	b
	☽P♇	6	43	D
	☽□♅	8	13	B

Date	Aspect	h	m	
11	☽⊻♄	8am	48	g
TH	☽⚼☿	2pm	33	b
	☽□♃	4	50	B
12	☽△♂	4am	32	G
F	☽△♆	9	39	G
	☽∠♄	10	7	b
	☉P☿	10	13	
	☽△♀	0pm	52	G
	☽P♃	7	28	G
	☽☍♇	10	55	B
	☽△♅	11	6	G
13	☉∠♅	4am	5	
S	☿⊻♀	6	18	
	☽⚼♂	7	35	b
	☽⚼♆	11	20	b
	☽✱♄	11	44	G
	☿⊥♅	1pm	41	
	☽⚼♀	3	27	b
	☽△♃	8	40	G
14	☽⚼♅	1am	2	b
SU	☽☍☉	2	37	B
	☉⊥♆	7	19	
	☽☍☿	2pm	40	B
	☽⚼♃	11	21	b
15	☿⊻♆	3am	15	
M	☿⊻♂	0pm	40	
	♀Q♄	1	53	
	☽□♄	4	37	B
16	♂☌♆	5am	19	
TU	☽⚼♇	6	36	b
	♄Stat	10	27	
	☽☍♆	8pm	0	B
	☽☍♂	8	54	B
	☿⊥♀	9	3	
	☿P♂	10	6	
17	☽☍♀	2am	57	B
W	☉☌☿	7	53	
	☽P♃	9	29	G
	☽△♇	10	44	G
	☽☍♅	11	1	B
	☽⚼☿	5pm	38	b
	☽⚼☉	7	40	b
18	☽△♄	0am	43	G
TH	☿⊥♂	7	46	
	☉⊥♀	11	24	
	☽☍♃	0pm	26	B

Date	Aspect	h	m	
	☽△☿	7	51	G
19	☽△☉	3am	34	G
F	☽⚼♄	6	6	b
	☿⊥♆	11	27	
	☽P♇	2pm	5	D
	♀P♆	8	21	
	☽□♇	9	38	B
20	♂Q♄	6am	7	
S	☿∠♅	6	30	
	☉⊻♆	9	35	
	☽⚼♆	0pm	9	b
	☽⚼♂	7	6	b
	☽⚼♀	9	40	b
21	☽□☿	2am	23	B
SU	☽⚼♅	4	25	b
	☽P♄	10	51	B
	☿✱♃	0pm	2	
	☽△♆	6	42	G
	☽□☉	9	43	B
22	☽△♂	3am	46	G
M	☽△♀	4	43	G
	☽⚼♃	8	22	b
	☽✱♇	10	39	G
	☉⊥♅	10	48	
	☽△♅	11	3	G
	☿P♆	0pm	2	
	♀☌♂	9	43	
23	☽P♄	1am	5	B
TU	☽☍♄	1	9	B
	☿∠♂	1	14	
	☿∠♀	3	39	
	☽✱☿	10	59	G
	☽△♃	3pm	15	G
	☽∠♇	5	5	b
	♀P♅	5	36	
24	☽□♆	7am	29	B
W	☽∠☿	3pm	32	b
	☽✱☉	3	49	G
	☽□♀	5	44	B
	☽□♂	8	18	B
	☽P♇	9	38	D
	☽⊻♇	10	59	g
	☽□♅	11	27	B
25	♂P♆	6am	21	
TH	☉⊻♀	4pm	11	
	☽⊻☿	7	56	g

Date	Aspect	h	m	
	☽∠☉	11	40	b
26	☽□♃	3am	10	B
F	☿P♂	0pm	32	
	♂✱♇	4	6	
	☽⚼♄	5	33	b
	☽✱♆	5	47	G
	☽P♃	7	20	G
	♀Stat	9	20	
27	♂☌♅	0am	39	
S	☽✱♀	3	29	G
	☽⊻☉	6	27	g
	☽☌♇	8	26	D
	☽✱♅	8	56	G
	☽✱♂	9	26	G
	☿Stat	11	39	
	☽△♄	9pm	24	G
	☽∠♆	9	39	b
28	☽☌☿	3am	40	G
SU	☉∠♃	4	20	
	☽∠♀	6	56	b
	☉⊻♇	8	25	
	☽P♀	10	27	G
	☽✱♃	11	40	G
	☽∠♅	0pm	24	b
	☽∠♂	2	29	b
	☉⊻♅	3	36	
29	☽⊻♆	0am	44	g
M	☽⊻♀	9	33	g
	☿P♆	11	22	
	☽⊻♇	2pm	36	g
	☽∠♃	2	44	b
	☽⊻♅	3	9	g
	☽☌☉	4	57	D
	☽⊻♂	6	42	g
	♂P♅	10	44	
30	☽□♄	2am	52	B
TU	☽⊻☿	9	46	g
	☽∠♇	4pm	45	b
	☽⊻♃	5	12	g
	☽P♀	7	34	G
31	☽☌♆	5am	7	D
W	☽∠☿	0pm	27	b
	☽☌♀	0	57	G
	☽✱♇	6	30	G
	☽☌♅	7	7	B
	☿∠♀	9	39	

Note. - To obtain Local Mean Time of aspect, add the time equivalent of the longitude if East and subtract if West.

G.M.T. AND EPHEMERIS TIME

The tabulations and times in this ephemeris are in G.M.T.

From 1960 to 1982 the tabulations were in Ephemeris Time (E.T.) but it should be pointed out that the maximum correction to phenomena or aspects using E.T. as compared with G.M.T. did not exceed 53 seconds and that any correction should be considered as negligible in normal use.

DISTANCES APART OF ALL ☌s AND ☍s IN 1997

Note: The Distances Apart are in Declination

JANUARY

1	☽ ☌ ♂	1am02	2	41
1	☽ ☍ ♄	5am13	2	15
2	☉ ☌ ☿	1am22	2	36
6	☽ ☌ ♇	3am21	7	49
7	☽ ☌ ♀	4pm43	4	30
8	☽ ☌ ☿	5am27	1	43
9	☽ ☌ ☉	4am26	4	45
9	♂ ☍ ♄	10am53	0	27
9	♃ ☌ ♆	11am40	0	45
9	☽ ☌ ♆	5pm29	4	2
9	☽ ☌ ♃	5pm33	4	47
10	☽ ☌ ♅	4am00	4	42
12	☿ ☌ ♀	2pm31	2	43
14	☽ ☌ ♄	2am58	2	3
14	☽ ☍ ♂	4am30	2	32
17	☉ ☌ ♆	0pm34	0	25
18	☽ ☍ ♇	8pm12	7	47
19	☉ ☌ ♃	1pm07	0	21
21	☽ ☍ ☿	10am28	3	23
22	☽ ☍ ♀	1am37	5	0
23	☽ ☍ ♆	3am09	4	1
23	☽ ☍ ♃	8am39	4	39
23	☽ ☍ ☉	3pm11	4	8
23	☽ ☍ ♅	5pm00	4	38
24	☉ ☌ ♅	1pm53	0	33
28	☽ ☍ ♄	4pm00	1	48
28	☽ ☌ ♂	8pm28	2	31

FEBRUARY

1	♀ ☌ ♆	2pm28	0	57
2	☽ ☌ ♇	2pm15	7	43
6	♀ ☌ ♃	1am48	0	19
6	☽ ☌ ☿	2am17	5	15
6	☽ ☌ ♆	6am29	4	2
6	☽ ☌ ♃	3pm17	4	32
6	☽ ☌ ♀	4pm16	4	50
6	☽ ☌ ♅	5pm53	4	37
7	♀ ☌ ♅	0pm44	0	11
7	☽ ☌ ☉	3pm06	3	12
8	☿ ☌ ♆	0am31	1	19
10	☽ ☌ ♄	3pm56	1	36
10	☽ ☍ ♂	5pm58	2	42
12	☿ ☌ ♃	6pm22	0	59
13	☿ ☌ ♅	3am57	0	51
15	☽ ☍ ♇	3am06	7	43
16	♃ ☌ ♅	2am22	0	10
16	♂ ☍ ♄	5pm14	1	19
19	☽ ☍ ♆	11am09	4	2
20	☽ ☍ ♅	2am16	4	36
20	☽ ☍ ♃	3am41	4	24
21	☽ ☍ ☿	2am36	5	9
21	☽ ☍ ♀	0pm17	4	1
22	☽ ☍ ☉	10am27	2	4
24	☽ ☌ ♂	10pm40	3	2
25	☽ ☍ ♄	3am42	1	24

MARCH

1	☽ ☌ ♇	10pm17	7	43
2	☿ ☌ ♀	2pm32	0	43
5	☽ ☌ ♆	6pm26	4	3
6	☽ ☌ ♅	7am04	4	35
6	☽ ☌ ♃	0pm04	4	16
8	☽ ☌ ♀	2pm36	2	44
8	☽ ☌ ☿	8pm56	2	46
9	☽ ● ☉	1am15	0	52
9	☽ ☍ ♂	6pm59	3	24
10	☽ ☌ ♄	7am55	1	15
11	☉ ☌ ☿	3pm34	1	27
14	☽ ☍ ♇	10am57	7	46
15	☿ ☍ ♂	0am06	2	19
17	☉ ☍ ♂	7am55	3	23
18	☽ ☍ ♆	7pm00	4	3
19	☽ ☍ ♅	11am14	4	34
19	♀ ☍ ♂	8pm08	2	2
19	☽ ☍ ♃	9pm54	4	7
20	☿ ☌ ♄	4pm15	1	42
23	☽ ☌ ♂	10am21	3	38
23	☽ ☍ ♀	11pm27	1	6
24	☽ ●–● ☉	4am45	0	25
24	☽ ☍ ♄	4pm26	1	6
25	☽ ☍ ☿	9am28	2	9
29	☽ ☌ ♇	3am49	7	51
30	☉ ☌ ♄	10pm20	2	1
31	♀ ☌ ♄	0pm48	0	48

APRIL

2	☽ ☌ ♆	3am30	4	1
2	☉ ☌ ♀	1pm45	1	11
2	☽ ☌ ♅	5pm25	4	32
3	☽ ☌ ♃	5am44	3	58
5	☽ ☍ ♂	2pm00	3	35
7	☽ ● ♄	0am23	0	58
7	☽ ☌ ☉	11am02	1	35
7	☽ ● ♀	1pm16	0	36
8	☽ ☌ ☿	8pm02	5	55
10	☽ ☍ ♇	7pm50	7	57
15	☽ ☍ ♆	3am07	3	58
15	☽ ☍ ♅	8pm08	4	28
16	☽ ☍ ♃	2pm46	3	48
19	☽ ☌ ♂	2am56	3	16
21	☽ ☍ ♄	6am08	0	50
22	☿ ☌ ♀	6am55	2	36
22	☽ ☍ ☉	8pm33	2	45
23	☽ ☍ ☿	4am09	4	45
23	☽ ☍ ♀	7am34	2	29
25	☽ ☌ ♇	8am41	8	3
25	☉ ☌ ☿	10am32	1	9
29	☽ ☌ ♆	9am46	3	53
30	☽ ☌ ♅	0am35	4	23
30	☽ ☌ ♃	7pm04	3	38

MAY

2	☽ ☍ ♂	5pm08	2	42
4	☽ ● ♄	3pm06	0	42
5	☽ ● ☿	4pm48	1	4
6	☽ ☌ ☉	8pm47	3	42
7	☽ ☌ ♀	1pm35	4	4
8	☽ ☍ ♇	4am34	8	7
12	☽ ☍ ♆	11am24	3	48
13	☽ ☍ ♅	4am44	4	18
14	☽ ☍ ♃	5am07	3	30
14	♀ ☍ ♇	9am45	12	50
16	☽ ☌ ♂	1pm49	1	58
18	☽ ☍ ♄	8pm12	0	33
20	☽ ☍ ☿	7am32	0	20
22	☽ ☍ ☉	9am13	4	29
22	☽ ☌ ♇	2pm36	8	9
23	☽ ☍ ♀	10am43	5	23
25	☉ ☍ ♇	9am57	12	45
26	☽ ☌ ♆	2pm59	3	42
27	☽ ☌ ♅	5am57	4	12
28	☽ ☌ ♃	4am10	3	22
30	☽ ☍ ♂	8am22	1	9

JUNE

1	☽ ● ♄	2am54	0	25
3	☽ ☌ ☿	1pm23	1	33
4	☽ ☍ ♇	11am55	8	8
5	☽ ☌ ☉	7am04	4	54
6	☽ ☌ ♀	4pm44	5	57
8	☽ ☍ ♆	7pm10	3	37
9	☽ ☍ ♅	0pm24	4	8
10	☽ ☍ ♃	3pm27	3	18
11	☿ ☍ ♇	2am04	11	22
13	☽ ● ♂	3pm45	0	15
15	☽ ☍ ♄	9am31	0	16
18	☽ ☌ ♇	10pm04	8	3
20	☽ ☍ ☿	6am43	5	20
20	☽ ☍ ☉	7pm09	4	59
22	☽ ☍ ♀	9am26	5	45
22	☽ ☌ ♆	9pm11	3	34
23	☽ ☌ ♅	11am39	4	4
24	☽ ☌ ♃	10am11	3	17
25	☉ ☌ ☿	7pm14	1	11
27	☽ ☍ ♂	8am49	0	39
28	♀ ☍ ♆	2am21	1	55
28	☽ ● ♄	11am54	0	9

JULY

1	☽ ☍ ♇	5pm32	7	56
4	☽ ☌ ☉	6pm40	4	42
5	♀ ☍ ♅	1am40	0	57
5	☽ ☌ ☿	6pm29	6	0
6	☽ ☍ ♆	1am45	3	33
6	☽ ☍ ♅	6pm36	4	3
6	☽ ☌ ♀	11pm16	4	50
7	☿ ☍ ♆	4pm04	2	14
7	☽ ☍ ♃	8pm44	3	19
12	☽ ☌ ♂	2am32	1	37
12	☿ ☍ ♅	5am55	1	1
12	☽ ☍ ♄	8pm40	0	2
15	♀ ☍ ♃	7am19	0	42
16	☽ ☌ ♇	6am33	7	45
19	☿ ☍ ♃	3pm12	0	5
20	☽ ☍ ☉	3am20	4	2
20	☽ ☌ ♆	5am12	3	34
20	☽ ☌ ♅	6pm56	4	4
21	☉ ☍ ♆	7am15	0	25
21	☽ ☌ ♃	2pm49	3	26
21	☽ ☍ ☿	8pm32	2	58
22	☽ ☍ ♀	5am24	3	19
25	☽ ☍ ♂	3pm55	2	30
25	☽ ● ♄	7pm14	0	1
28	☽ ☍ ♇	10pm20	7	35
29	♂ ☍ ♄	3am25	2	41
29	☉ ☍ ♅	7pm29	0	38

AUGUST

2	☽ ☍ ♆	7am01	3	35
2	☽ ☍ ♅	11pm19	4	6
3	☽ ☌ ☉	8am14	3	9
3	☽ ☍ ♃	9pm36	3	34
5	☽ ● ☿	7pm44	0	53
6	☽ ☌ ♀	7am51	1	25
9	☽ ☍ ♄	4am28	0	3
9	☉ ☍ ♃	1pm40	0	56
9	☽ ☌ ♂	6pm16	3	27
12	☽ ☌ ♇	3pm01	7	23
16	☽ ☌ ♆	2pm31	3	39
17	☽ ☌ ♅	3am40	4	9
17	☽ ☌ ♃	7pm38	3	45
18	☽ ☍ ☉	10am55	2	2
19	☽ ☍ ☿	7pm28	3	37
21	☽ ☍ ♀	0am15	0	39
22	☽ ● ♄	2am18	0	0
23	☽ ☍ ♂	4am14	4	14
25	☽ ☍ ♇	4am04	7	14
29	☽ ☍ ♆	11am35	3	42
30	☽ ☍ ♅	3am16	4	12
30	☽ ☍ ♃	8pm56	3	53
31	☉ ☌ ☿	1pm43	3	43

SEPTEMBER

1	☽ ☌ ☿	6pm48	2	24
1	☽ ● ☉	11pm52	0	52
3	♀ ☍ ♄	2am26	2	37
5	☽ ☍ ♄	8am48	0	4
5	☽ ☌ ♀	3pm00	2	56
7	☽ ☌ ♂	0pm44	5	2
8	☽ ☌ ♇	10pm40	7	5
12	☽ ☌ ♆	11pm45	3	44
13	☽ ☌ ♅	0pm40	4	15
14	☽ ☌ ♃	1am40	4	0
15	☽ ☍ ☿	0pm51	1	32
16	☽ ●–● ☉	6pm50	0	21
18	☽ ● ♄	9am53	0	10
19	☽ ☍ ♀	6pm58	4	57
20	☽ ☍ ♂	9pm03	5	37
21	☽ ☍ ♇	0pm17	6	59
25	☽ ☍ ♆	4pm45	3	44
26	☽ ☍ ♅	7am52	4	15
26	☽ ☍ ♃	10pm42	4	2
30	☽ ☌ ☿	6pm08	1	5

OCTOBER

1	☽ ☌ ☉	4pm52	1	34
2	☽ ☍ ♄	10am58	0	17
3	♂ ☌ ♇	11pm44	12	58
5	☽ ☌ ♀	5pm01	6	54
6	☽ ☌ ♇	5am38	6	56
6	☽ ☌ ♂	8am44	6	5
10	☉ ☍ ♄	4am26	2	33
10	☽ ☌ ♆	7am35	3	41
10	☽ ☌ ♅	8pm39	4	12
11	☽ ☌ ♃	9am11	3	59
11	☿ ☍ ♄	4pm28	1	28
11	♀ ☌ ♇	5pm41	14	24
13	☉ ☌ ☿	9pm02	0	54
15	☽ ● ♄	5pm38	0	22
16	☽ ☍ ☉	3am46	2	40
16	☽ ☍ ☿	6am39	2	8
18	☽ ☍ ♇	11pm11	6	53
19	☽ ☍ ♀	1pm31	8	5
19	☽ ☍ ♂	5pm50	6	19
22	☽ ☍ ♆	11pm48	3	38
23	☽ ☍ ♅	2pm30	4	8
24	☽ ☍ ♃	5am49	3	53
26	♀ ☌ ♂	11am34	2	5

DISTANCES APART OF ALL ☌s AND ☍s IN 1997

Note: The Distances Apart are in Declination

Day	Aspect	Time	Distance
29	☽☍♄	1pm15	0 25
31	☽☌☉	10am01	3 41
NOVEMBER			
1	☽☌☿	10am13	5 23
2	☽☌♇	0pm59	6 53
4	☽☌♂	5am38	6 17
4	☽☌♀	10am48	8 33
6	☽☌♆	1pm58	3 30
7	☽☌♅	3am19	3 59
7	☽☌♃	6pm24	3 39
11	☿☌♇	0am17	13 40
12	☽●♄	0am35	0 24
14	☽☍☉	2pm12	4 25
15	☽☍♇	11am27	6 52
15	☽☍☿	11pm10	7 16
17	☽☍♂	6pm01	6 1
18	☽☍♀	4am41	8 5
19	☽☍♆	9am10	3 24
19	☽☍♅	11pm47	3 52
20	☽☍♃	6pm51	3 25
25	☽☍♄	5pm40	0 19
27	☉☌♇	4pm34	11 42
29	☽☌♇	9pm52	6 51
30	☽☌☉	2am14	4 54
DECEMBER			
1	☽☌☿	8pm11	6 55
3	☽☌♂	3am12	5 25
3	☽☌♀	2pm52	6 31
3	☽☌♆	8pm29	3 15
4	☽☌♅	10am08	3 41
5	☽☌♃	6am02	3 6
8	♀☌♆	7pm31	2 33
9	☽●♄	6am22	0 11
12	☽☍♇	10pm55	6 49
14	☽☍☉	2am37	4 57
14	☽☍☿	2pm40	3 46
16	♂☌♆	5am19	1 34
16	☽☍♆	8pm00	3 9
16	☽☍♂	8pm54	4 41
17	☽☍♀	2am57	4 20
17	☉☌☿	7am53	1 56
17	☽☍♅	11am01	3 33
18	☽☍♃	0pm26	2 48
22	♀☌♂	9pm43	1 8
23	☽☍♄	1am09	0 1
27	♂☌♅	0am39	0 34
27	☽☌♇	8am26	6 47
28	☽☌☿	3am40	2 6
29	☽☌☉	4pm57	4 34
31	☽☌♆	5am07	3 4
31	☽☌♀	0pm57	1 13
31	☽☌♅	7pm07	3 25

TIME WHEN THE SUN. MOON AND PLANETS ENTER THE ZODIACAL SIGNS IN 1997

JANUARY

Day	Sign	Time
1	☽♎	2am31
3	♂♎	8am11
3	☽♏	1pm01
5	☽♐	7pm26
7	☽♑	9pm54
9	☽♒	10pm00
10	♀♑	5am32
11	☽♓	9pm51
13	☽♈	11pm22
16	☽♉	3am41
18	☽♊	10am53
20	☉♒	0am42
20	☽♋	8pm29
21	♃♒	3pm13
23	☽♌	7am50
25	☽♍	8pm26
28	☽♎	9am21
30	☽♏	8pm47

FEBRUARY

Day	Sign	Time
2	☽♐	4am49
3	♀♒	4am28
4	☽♑	8am43
6	☽♒	9am21
8	☽♓	8am34
9	☿♒	5am53
10	☽♈	8am30
12	☽♉	10am57
14	☽♊	4pm54
17	☽♋	2am13
18	☉♓	2pm52
19	☽♌	1pm53
22	☽♍	2am38
24	☽♎	3pm23
27	☽♏	2am56
27	♀♓	4am01
28	☿♓	3am54

MARCH

Day	Sign	Time
1	☽♐	0pm01
3	☽♑	5pm37
5	☽♒	7pm54
7	☽♓	7pm57
8	♂♍	7pm49
9	☽♈	7pm33
11	☽♉	8pm38
14	☽♊	0am49
16	☿♈	4am13
16	☽♋	8am51
18	☽♌	8pm09
20	☉♈	1pm55
21	☽♍	8am59
23	♀♈	5am26
23	☽♎	9pm35
26	☽♏	8am41
28	☽♐	5pm39
31	☽♑	0am07

APRIL

Day	Sign	Time
1	☿♉	1pm46
2	☽♒	3am58
4	☽♓	5am42
6	☽♈	6am19
8	☽♉	7am21
10	☽♊	10am28
12	☽♋	5pm05
15	☽♌	3am22
16	♀♉	9am43
17	☽♍	4pm00
20	☉♉	1am03
20	☽♎	4am36
22	☽♏	3pm18
24	☽♐	11pm32
27	☽♑	5am32
29	☽♒	9am50

MAY

Day	Sign	Time
1	☽♓	0pm50
3	☽♈	2pm59
5	☿♈	1am55
5	☽♉	5pm05
7	☽♊	8pm21
10	☽♋	2am13
10	♀♊	5pm20
12	☿♉	10am20
12	☽♌	11am33
14	☽♍	11pm43
17	☽♎	0pm27
19	☽♏	11pm11
21	☉♊	0am18
22	☽♐	6am50
24	☽♑	11am51
26	☽♒	3pm20
28	☽♓	6pm18
30	☽♈	9pm18

JUNE

Day	Sign	Time
2	☽♉	0am39
4	♀♋	4am18
4	☽♊	4am55
6	☽♋	11am02
8	☽♌	7pm59
8	☿♊	11pm25
11	☽♍	7am43
13	☽♎	8pm35
16	☽♏	7am50
18	☽♐	3pm38
19	♂♎	8am30
20	☽♑	8pm02
21	☉♋	8am20
22	☽♒	10pm20
23	☿♋	8pm41
25	☽♓	0am09
27	☽♈	2am39
28	♀♌	6pm38
29	☽♉	6am24

JULY

Day	Sign	Time
1	☽♊	11am35
3	☽♋	6pm33
6	☽♌	3am46
8	☿♌	5am28
8	☽♍	3pm22
11	☽♎	4am20
13	☽♏	4pm19
16	☽♐	1am02
18	☽♑	5am44
20	☽♒	7am28
22	☽♓	8am00
22	☉♌	7pm15
23	♀♍	1pm16
24	☽♈	9am03
26	☽♉	11am53
27	☿♍	0am42
28	☽♊	5pm05
31	☽♋	0am38

AUGUST

Day	Sign	Time
2	☽♌	10am27
4	☽♍	10pm15
7	☽♎	11am17
9	☽♏	11pm50
12	☽♐	9am44
14	♂♏	8am42
14	☽♑	3pm41
16	☽♒	5pm57
17	♀♎	2pm31
18	☽♓	6pm01
20	☽♈	5pm45
22	☽♉	6pm58
23	☉♍	2am19
24	☽♊	10pm56
27	☽♋	6am11
29	☽♌	4pm19

SEPTEMBER

Day	Sign	Time
1	☽♍	4am27
3	☽♎	5pm29
6	☽♏	6am09
8	☽♐	4pm53
11	☽♑	0am23
12	♀♏	2am17
13	☽♒	4am09
15	☽♓	4am59
17	☽♈	4am25
19	☽♉	4am22
21	☽♊	6am40
22	☉♎	11pm56
23	☽♋	0pm33
25	☽♌	10pm13
28	☽♍	10am27
28	♂♐	10pm22
30	☽♎	11pm32

OCTOBER

Day	Sign	Time
2	☿♎	5am38
3	☽♏	11am57
5	☽♐	10pm42
8	☽♑	7am03
8	♀♐	8am25
10	☽♒	0pm28
12	☽♓	2pm59
14	☽♈	3pm25
16	☽♉	3pm16
18	☽♊	4pm28
19	☿♏	0pm08
20	☽♋	8pm46
23	☽♌	5am11
23	☉♏	9am15
25	☽♍	5pm00
28	☽♎	6am05
30	☽♏	6pm15

NOVEMBER

Day	Sign	Time
2	☽♐	4am26
4	☽♑	0pm31
5	♀♑	8am50
6	☽♒	6pm33
7	☿♐	5pm42
8	☽♓	10pm34
9	♂♑	5am33
11	☽♈	0am43
13	☽♉	1am45
15	☽♊	3am05
17	☽♋	6am33
19	☽♌	1pm38
22	☽♍	0am33
22	☉♐	6am48
24	☽♎	1pm29
27	☽♏	1am43
29	☽♐	11am28
30	☿♑	7pm15

DECEMBER

Day	Sign	Time
1	☽♑	6pm38
3	☽♒	11pm58
6	☽♓	4am07
8	☽♈	7am23
10	☽♉	10am00
12	♀♒	4am41
12	☽♊	0pm35
13	☿♐	6pm00
14	☽♋	4pm26
16	☽♌	10pm58
18	♂♒	6am37
19	☽♍	9am00
21	☉♑	8pm07
21	☽♎	9pm35
24	☽♏	10am07
26	☽♐	8pm06
29	☽♑	2am48
31	☽♒	6am58

LOCAL MEAN TIME OF SUNRISE FOR LATITUDES
60° North to 50° South

FOR ALL SUNDAYS IN 1997. (ALL TIMES ARE A.M.)

Date	NORTHERN LATITUDES									SOUTHERN LATITUDES				
	LONDON	60°	55°	50°	40°	30°	20°	10°	0°	10°	20°	30°	40°	50°
1996	H M	H M	H M	H M	H M	H M	H M	H M	H M	H M	H M	H M	H M	H M
Dec. 29	8 6	9 4	8 26	7 59	7 21	6 55	6 34	6 16	5 58	5 41	5 22	5 0	4 33	3 52
1997														
Jan. 5	8 5	9 0	8 24	7 58	7 22	6 57	6 36	6 18	6 2	5 45	5 27	5 5	4 39	4 0
,, 12	8 1	8 52	8 19	7 55	7 21	6 57	6 38	6 21	6 5	5 48	5 31	5 11	4 45	4 9
,, 19	7 55	8 41	8 11	7 50	7 18	6 56	6 38	6 22	6 7	5 52	5 35	5 17	4 53	4 19
,, 26	7 47	8 28	8 2	7 42	7 14	6 54	6 37	6 23	6 9	5 55	5 40	5 23	5 1	4 31
Feb. 2	7 38	8 12	7 50	7 33	7 8	6 50	6 35	6 23	6 10	5 58	5 45	5 29	5 10	4 43
,, 9	7 25	7 55	7 36	7 22	7 1	6 45	6 33	6 21	6 11	6 0	5 49	5 35	5 19	4 55
,, 16	7 12	7 36	7 21	7 9	6 52	6 39	6 29	6 20	6 11	6 2	5 52	5 41	5 27	5 8
,, 23	6 59	7 17	7 5	6 56	6 43	6 33	6 24	6 17	6 10	6 3	5 55	5 47	5 35	5 20
Mar. 2	6 43	6 56	6 48	6 42	6 32	6 25	6 19	6 14	6 9	6 4	5 58	5 51	5 43	5 32
,, 9	6 28	6 36	6 31	6 27	6 22	6 17	6 14	6 11	6 7	6 4	6 0	5 56	5 51	5 44
,, 16	6 12	6 15	6 13	6 12	6 11	6 9	6 8	6 7	6 6	6 4	6 2	6 1	5 58	5 55
,, 23	5 57	5 53	5 55	5 57	5 59	6 1	6 2	6 3	6 3	6 4	6 4	6 5	6 6	6 6
,, 30	5 41	5 32	5 38	5 42	5 48	5 52	5 56	5 59	6 1	6 4	6 6	6 9	6 13	6 17
April 6	5 25	5 11	5 20	5 27	5 37	5 44	5 50	5 55	5 59	6 4	6 8	6 13	6 20	6 28
,, 13	5 9	4 50	5 2	5 12	5 26	5 36	5 44	5 51	5 57	6 4	6 10	6 17	6 27	6 39
,, 20	4 55	4 30	4 46	4 58	5 15	5 28	5 38	5 47	5 56	6 4	6 12	6 22	6 34	6 50
,, 27	4 41	4 10	4 29	4 44	5 6	5 21	5 34	5 44	5 54	6 4	6 14	6 26	6 41	7 0
May 4	4 28	3 51	4 14	4 32	4 57	5 15	5 29	5 42	5 53	6 5	6 17	6 30	6 48	7 11
,, 11	4 15	3 33	4 0	4 20	4 49	5 9	5 26	5 40	5 53	6 6	6 19	6 35	6 54	7 21
,, 18	4 4	3 16	3 48	4 10	4 42	5 5	5 23	5 38	5 53	6 7	6 22	6 39	7 1	7 30
,, 25	3 56	3 2	3 37	4 2	4 37	5 2	5 21	5 38	5 53	6 9	6 25	6 43	7 7	7 39
June 1	3 49	2 50	3 29	3 56	4 33	4 59	5 20	5 38	5 54	6 10	6 28	6 47	7 12	7 47
,, 8	3 45	2 41	3 23	3 52	4 31	4 58	5 20	5 38	5 55	6 12	6 30	6 51	7 17	7 53
,, 15	3 42	2 36	3 20	3 50	4 30	4 58	5 20	5 39	5 57	6 14	6 32	6 54	7 20	7 57
,, 22	3 42	2 35	3 20	3 50	4 31	4 59	5 21	5 40	5 58	6 16	6 34	6 56	7 22	8 0
,, 29	3 45	2 40	3 24	3 53	4 34	5 2	5 23	5 42	6 0	6 17	6 35	6 56	7 23	8 0
July 6	3 51	2 48	3 30	3 58	4 37	5 4	5 26	5 44	6 1	6 18	6 36	6 56	7 21	7 58
,, 13	3 58	2 59	3 38	4 5	4 42	5 8	5 28	5 46	6 2	6 18	6 35	6 55	7 19	7 53
,, 20	4 6	3 13	3 48	4 13	4 47	5 12	5 31	5 47	6 3	6 18	6 34	6 53	7 15	7 47
,, 27	4 16	3 28	3 59	4 22	4 53	5 16	5 33	5 49	6 3	6 17	6 32	6 49	7 10	7 38
Aug. 3	4 26	3 45	4 12	4 32	5 0	5 20	5 36	5 50	6 3	6 15	6 29	6 44	7 3	7 29
,, 10	4 38	4 1	4 25	4 42	5 6	5 24	5 38	5 51	6 2	6 13	6 25	6 38	6 55	7 17
,, 17	4 48	4 18	4 38	4 52	5 13	5 28	5 40	5 51	6 1	6 10	6 20	6 32	6 45	7 4
,, 24	4 59	4 35	4 51	5 2	5 20	5 32	5 42	5 51	5 59	6 7	6 15	6 25	6 36	6 51
,, 31	5 10	4 52	5 4	5 13	5 26	5 36	5 44	5 51	5 57	6 3	6 9	6 17	6 25	6 37
Sept. 7	5 22	5 8	5 17	5 23	5 33	5 40	5 46	5 50	5 55	5 59	6 4	6 8	6 15	6 22
,, 14	5 33	5 25	5 30	5 34	5 40	5 44	5 47	5 50	5 52	5 55	5 57	6 0	6 3	6 7
,, 21	5 44	5 41	5 43	5 44	5 46	5 48	5 49	5 49	5 50	5 50	5 51	5 51	5 51	5 52
,, 28	5 55	5 58	5 56	5 55	5 53	5 51	5 50	5 49	5 48	5 46	5 45	5 42	5 40	5 36
Oct. 5	6 6	6 14	6 9	6 6	6 0	5 55	5 52	5 48	5 45	5 42	5 38	5 34	5 29	5 21
,, 12	6 18	6 31	6 23	6 17	6 7	6 0	5 54	5 48	5 43	5 38	5 32	5 26	5 17	5 6
,, 19	6 31	6 49	6 37	6 28	6 14	6 4	5 56	5 49	5 42	5 34	5 27	5 18	5 7	4 52
,, 26	6 42	7 6	6 51	6 39	6 22	6 9	5 59	5 49	5 41	5 32	5 22	5 11	4 57	4 38
Nov. 2	6 55	7 24	7 5	6 51	6 30	6 14	6 2	5 51	5 40	5 30	5 18	5 5	4 48	4 25
,, 9	7 8	7 42	7 20	7 3	6 38	6 20	6 5	5 53	5 40	5 28	5 15	5 0	4 40	4 14
,, 16	7 20	8 0	7 34	7 14	6 46	6 26	6 9	5 55	5 41	5 28	5 13	4 56	4 34	4 4
, 23	7 31	8 17	7 47	7 25	6 54	6 32	6 13	5 58	5 43	5 28	5 12	4 53	4 29	3 56
,, 30	7 41	8 33	7 59	7 35	7 1	6 37	6 18	6 1	5 45	5 29	5 12	4 51	4 26	3 50
Dec. 7	7 51	8 46	8 10	7 44	7 8	6 43	6 22	6 4	5 48	5 31	5 13	4 51	4 25	3 46
,, 14	7 58	8 56	8 18	7 51	7 14	6 48	6 27	6 8	5 51	5 34	5 15	4 53	4 25	3 45
,, 21	8 3	9 2	8 23	7 56	7 18	6 52	6 30	6 12	5 54	5 37	5 18	4 56	4 28	3 47
,, 28	8 5	9 4	8 25	7 58	7 21	6 55	6 34	6 15	5 58	5 40	5 22	4 59	4 32	3 51
1998														
Jan. 4	8 5	9 1	8 24	7 58	7 22	6 57	6 36	6 18	6 2	5 44	5 25	5 4	4 37	3 58

Example:—To find the time of Sunrise in Jamaica (Latitude 18° N.) on Friday, June 27th, 1997. On June 22nd, L.M.T. = 5h. 21m. + $\frac{2}{10}$ × 19m. = 5h. 25m., on June 29th L.M.T. = 5h. 23m. + $\frac{2}{10}$ × 19m. = 5h. 27m., therefore L.M.T. on June 27th = 5h. 25m. + $\frac{5}{7}$ × 2m. = 5h. 26m. A.M.

LOCAL MEAN TIME OF SUNSET FOR LATITUDES
60° North to 50° South

FOR ALL SUNDAYS IN 1997. (ALL TIMES ARE P.M.)

Date	NORTHERN LATITUDES									SOUTHERN LATITUDES				
	LONDON	60°	55°	50°	40°	30°	20°	10°	0°	10°	20°	30°	40°	50°
1996	H M	H M	H M	H M	H M	H M	H M	H M	H M	H M	H M	H M	H M	H M
Dec. 29	3 59	3 1	3 39	4 6	4 43	5 9	5 30	5 49	6 6	6 23	6 42	7 4	7 32	8 12
1997														
Jan. 5	4 6	3 11	3 47	4 13	4 49	5 14	5 35	5 52	6 9	6 26	6 44	7 6	7 33	8 11
,, 12	4 16	3 25	3 58	4 22	4 56	5 20	5 39	5 56	6 12	6 28	6 46	7 6	7 31	8 7
,, 19	4 27	3 41	4 11	4 32	5 4	5 26	5 44	6 0	6 15	6 30	6 46	7 4	7 28	8 1
,, 26	4 39	3 58	4 24	4 44	5 12	5 32	5 48	6 3	6 16	6 30	6 45	7 2	7 23	7 53
Feb. 2	4 51	4 16	4 39	4 56	5 20	5 38	5 52	6 5	6 17	6 30	6 43	6 58	7 17	7 43
,, 9	5 4	4 35	4 54	5 8	5 29	5 44	5 56	6 7	6 18	6 28	6 40	6 53	7 9	7 32
,, 16	5 17	4 53	5 8	5 20	5 37	5 49	6 0	6 9	6 18	6 26	6 36	6 47	7 1	7 19
,, 23	5 29	5 12	5 23	5 32	5 45	5 55	6 3	6 10	6 17	6 24	6 31	6 40	6 51	7 5
Mar. 2	5 42	5 29	5 37	5 43	5 53	6 0	6 5	6 11	6 16	6 21	6 26	6 32	6 41	6 51
,, 9	5 54	5 47	5 51	5 55	6 0	6 4	6 8	6 11	6 14	6 17	6 20	6 24	6 30	6 37
,, 16	6 6	6 4	6 5	6 6	6 8	6 9	6 10	6 11	6 12	6 13	6 14	6 16	6 18	6 22
,, 23	6 18	6 21	6 19	6 17	6 15	6 13	6 12	6 11	6 10	6 9	6 8	6 8	6 7	6 6
,, 30	6 29	6 38	6 33	6 28	6 22	6 17	6 14	6 11	6 8	6 5	6 2	5 59	5 56	5 51
April 6	6 41	6 56	6 46	6 39	6 29	6 22	6 16	6 11	6 6	6 1	5 56	5 51	5 45	5 36
,, 13	6 53	7 13	7 0	6 50	6 36	6 26	6 18	6 11	6 4	5 57	5 51	5 43	5 34	5 22
,, 20	7 5	7 30	7 14	7 1	6 43	6 30	6 20	6 11	6 2	5 54	5 45	5 36	5 24	5 8
,, 27	7 16	7 47	7 27	7 12	6 50	6 35	6 22	6 11	6 1	5 51	5 41	5 29	5 14	4 55
May 4	7 27	8 5	7 41	7 23	6 57	6 39	6 25	6 12	6 0	5 49	5 37	5 23	5 5	4 43
,, 11	7 39	8 22	7 54	7 33	7 4	6 44	6 27	6 13	6 0	5 47	5 33	5 17	4 58	4 31
,, 18	7 49	8 38	8 6	7 43	7 11	6 48	6 30	6 14	6 0	5 46	5 30	5 13	4 52	4 22
,, 25	7 59	8 54	8 18	7 52	7 17	6 52	6 33	6 16	6 0	5 45	5 28	5 10	4 47	4 14
June 1	8 7	9 7	8 28	8 0	7 22	6 56	6 36	6 18	6 1	5 45	5 28	5 8	4 43	4 9
,, 8	8 14	9 18	8 35	8 6	7 27	7 0	6 38	6 20	6 3	5 46	5 28	5 7	4 41	4 5
,, 15	8 19	9 25	8 41	8 11	7 30	7 2	6 40	6 22	6 4	5 47	5 28	5 7	4 41	4 3
,, 22	8 21	9 28	8 43	8 13	7 32	7 4	6 42	6 23	6 6	5 48	5 30	5 8	4 42	4 4
,, 29	8 21	9 26	8 43	8 13	7 33	7 5	6 43	6 25	6 7	5 50	5 32	5 10	4 44	4 7
July 6	8 18	9 21	8 39	8 11	7 32	7 5	6 44	6 25	6 8	5 52	5 34	5 13	4 47	4 12
,, 13	8 13	9 11	8 33	8 6	7 29	7 3	6 43	6 26	6 9	5 53	5 36	5 17	4 52	4 18
,, 20	8 5	8 58	8 24	7 59	7 25	7 1	6 42	6 25	6 10	5 55	5 38	5 21	4 58	4 26
,, 27	7 56	8 43	8 12	7 50	7 19	6 57	6 39	6 24	6 10	5 56	5 41	5 25	5 4	4 35
Aug. 3	7 45	8 26	7 59	7 40	7 12	6 52	6 36	6 22	6 10	5 57	5 44	5 29	5 10	4 44
,, 10	7 32	8 8	7 45	7 28	7 4	6 46	6 32	6 20	6 9	5 58	5 46	5 33	5 16	4 54
,, 17	7 19	7 48	7 29	7 15	6 54	6 39	6 28	6 17	6 7	5 58	5 48	5 37	5 23	5 4
,, 24	7 4	7 28	7 13	7 1	6 44	6 32	6 22	6 14	6 6	5 58	5 50	5 40	5 29	5 14
,, 31	6 49	7 7	6 56	6 47	6 34	6 24	6 16	6 10	6 4	5 58	5 51	5 44	5 36	5 24
Sept. 7	6 33	6 46	6 38	6 32	6 22	6 16	6 10	6 6	6 1	5 57	5 53	5 48	5 42	5 35
,, 14	6 17	6 25	6 20	6 16	6 11	6 7	6 4	6 1	5 59	5 57	5 54	5 52	5 49	5 45
,, 21	6 1	6 4	6 2	6 1	5 59	5 58	5 57	5 57	5 56	5 56	5 56	5 56	5 55	5 55
,, 28	5 45	5 42	5 44	5 46	5 48	5 50	5 51	5 53	5 54	5 55	5 58	5 59	6 2	6 6
Oct. 5	5 30	5 21	5 27	5 30	5 36	5 41	5 45	5 48	5 52	5 55	5 59	6 3	6 9	6 17
,, 12	5 14	5 1	5 9	5 16	5 26	5 33	5 39	5 45	5 50	5 55	6 1	6 8	6 16	6 28
,, 19	4 59	4 40	4 52	5 2	5 15	5 25	5 34	5 41	5 48	5 56	6 4	6 13	6 24	6 39
,, 26	4 45	4 21	4 36	4 48	5 6	5 19	5 29	5 39	5 47	5 57	6 6	6 18	6 32	6 51
Nov. 2	4 32	4 2	4 21	4 36	4 57	5 12	5 25	5 36	5 47	5 58	6 10	6 23	6 40	7 3
,, 9	4 20	3 45	4 8	4 25	4 49	5 8	5 22	5 35	5 47	6 0	6 13	6 28	6 48	7 15
,, 16	4 10	3 29	3 55	4 15	4 43	5 4	5 20	5 35	5 48	6 2	6 17	6 34	6 56	7 27
,, 23	4 2	3 15	3 46	4 7	4 39	5 1	5 19	5 35	5 50	6 5	6 22	6 40	7 4	7 38
,, 30	3 56	3 4	3 38	4 2	4 36	5 0	5 19	5 36	5 52	6 9	6 26	6 46	7 12	7 48
Dec. 7	3 52	2 57	3 33	3 59	4 35	5 0	5 21	5 38	5 55	6 12	6 30	6 52	7 19	7 57
,, 14	3 51	2 53	3 31	3 58	4 35	5 2	5 23	5 41	5 58	6 16	6 35	6 57	7 25	8 5
,, 21	3 53	2 54	3 33	4 0	4 38	5 4	5 25	5 44	6 1	6 19	6 38	7 1	7 29	8 9
,, 28	3 58	3 0	3 38	4 5	4 42	5 9	5 30	5 48	6 5	6 23	6 42	7 4	7 31	8 12
1998														
Jan. 4	4 4	3 9	3 46	4 12	4 48	5 13	5 34	5 52	6 9	6 26	6 44	7 5	7 32	8 11

Example:—To find the time of Sunset at Canberra (Latitude 35°·3S.) on Wednesday, August 6th, 1997. On August 3rd, L.M.T. = 5h. 29m. —$\frac{5\cdot 3}{10}$ × 19m. = 5h. 19m., on August 10th, L.M.T. = 5h. 33m. — $\frac{5\cdot 3}{10}$ × 17 m. = 5h. 24m., therefore L.M.T. on August 6th = 5h. 19m. +$\frac{3}{7}$ × 5^{m} = 5h. 21m. P.M.

TABLES OF HOUSES FOR LONDON, *Latitude* 51° 32′ *N.*

Sidereal Time.			10 ♈	11 ♉	12 ♊	Ascen ♋		2 ♌	3 ♍
H.	M.	S.	°	°	°	°	′	°	°
0	0	0	0	9	22	26	36	12	3
0	3	40	1	10	23	27	17	13	3
0	7	20	2	11	24	27	56	14	4
0	11	0	3	12	25	28	42	15	5
0	14	41	4	13	25	29	17	15	6
0	18	21	5	14	26	29	55	16	7
0	22	2	6	15	27	0 ♌	34	17	8
0	25	42	7	16	28	1	14	18	8
0	29	23	8	17	29	1	55	18	9
0	33	4	9	18	♋	2	33	19	10
0	36	45	10	19	1	3	14	20	11
0	40	26	11	20	1	3	54	20	12
0	44	8	12	21	2	4	33	21	13
0	47	50	13	22	3	5	12	22	14
0	51	32	14	23	4	5	52	23	15
0	55	14	15	24	5	6	30	23	15
0	58	57	16	25	6	7	9	24	16
1	2	40	17	26	6	7	50	25	17
1	6	23	18	27	7	8	30	26	18
1	10	7	19	28	8	9	9	26	19
1	13	51	20	29	9	9	48	27	19
1	17	35	21	♊	10	10	28	28	20
1	21	20	22	1	10	11	8	28	21
1	25	6	23	2	11	11	48	29	22
1	28	52	24	3	12	12	28	♍	23
1	32	38	25	4	13	13	8	1	24
1	36	25	26	5	14	13	48	1	25
1	40	12	27	6	14	14	28	2	25
1	44	0	28	7	15	15	8	3	26
1	47	48	29	8	16	15	48	4	27
1	51	37	30	9	17	16	28	4	28

Sidereal Time.			10 ♉	11 ♊	12 ♋	Ascen ♌		2 ♍	3 ♍
H.	M.	S.	°	°	°	°	′	°	°
1	51	37	0	9	17	16	28	4	28
1	55	27	1	10	18	17	8	5	29
1	59	17	2	11	19	17	48	6	♎
2	3	8	3	12	19	18	28	7	1
2	6	59	4	13	20	19	9	8	2
2	10	51	5	14	21	19	49	9	2
2	14	44	6	15	22	20	29	9	3
2	18	37	7	16	22	21	10	10	4
2	22	31	8	17	23	21	51	11	5
2	26	25	9	18	24	22	32	11	6
2	30	20	10	19	25	23	14	12	7
2	34	16	11	20	25	23	55	13	8
2	38	13	12	21	26	24	36	14	9
2	42	10	13	22	27	25	17	15	10
2	46	8	14	23	28	25	58	15	11
2	50	7	15	24	29	26	40	16	12
2	54	7	16	25	29	27	22	17	12
2	58	7	17	26	♌	28	4	18	13
3	2	8	18	27	1	28	46	18	14
3	6	9	19	27	2	29	28	19	15
3	10	12	20	28	3	0 ♍	12	20	16
3	14	15	21	29	3	0	54	21	17
3	18	19	22	♋	4	1	36	22	18
3	22	23	23	1	5	2	20	22	19
3	26	29	24	2	6	3	2	23	20
3	30	35	25	3	7	3	45	24	21
3	34	41	26	4	7	4	28	25	22
3	38	49	27	5	8	5	11	26	23
3	42	57	28	6	9	5	54	27	24
3	47	6	29	7	10	6	38	27	25
3	51	15	30	8	11	7	21	28	25

Sidereal Time.			10 ♊	11 ♋	12 ♌	Ascen ♍		2 ♍	3 ♎
H.	M.	S.	°	°	°	°	′	°	°
3	51	15	0	8	11	7	21	28	25
3	55	25	1	9	12	8	5	29	26
3	59	36	2	10	12	8	49	♎	27
4	3	48	3	10	13	9	33	1	28
4	8	0	4	11	14	10	17	2	29
4	12	13	5	12	15	11	2	2	♏
4	16	26	6	13	16	11	46	3	1
4	20	40	7	14	17	12	30	4	2
4	24	55	8	15	17	13	15	5	3
4	29	10	9	16	18	14	0	6	4
4	33	26	10	17	19	14	45	7	5
4	37	42	11	18	20	15	30	8	6
4	41	59	12	19	21	16	15	8	7
4	46	16	13	20	21	17	0	9	8
4	50	34	14	21	22	17	45	10	9
4	54	52	15	22	23	18	30	11	10
4	59	10	16	23	24	19	16	12	11
5	3	29	17	24	25	20	3	13	12
5	7	49	18	25	26	20	49	14	13
5	12	9	19	25	27	21	35	14	14
5	16	29	20	26	28	22	20	15	14
5	20	49	21	27	28	23	6	16	15
5	25	9	22	28	29	23	51	17	16
5	29	30	23	29	♍	24	37	18	17
5	33	51	24	♌	1	25	23	19	18
5	38	12	25	1	2	26	9	20	19
5	42	34	26	2	3	26	55	21	20
5	46	55	27	3	4	27	41	21	21
5	51	17	28	4	4	28	27	22	22
5	55	38	29	5	5	29	13	23	23
6	0	0	30	6	6	30	0	24	24

Sidereal Time.			10 ♋	11 ♌	12 ♍	Ascen ♎		2 ♎	3 ♏
H.	M.	S.	°	°	°	°	′	°	°
6	0	0	0	6	6	0	0	24	24
6	4	22	1	7	7	0	47	25	25
6	8	43	2	8	8	1	33	26	26
6	13	5	3	9	9	2	19	27	27
6	17	26	4	10	10	3	5	27	28
6	21	48	5	11	10	3	51	28	29
6	26	9	6	12	11	4	37	29	♐
6	30	30	7	13	12	5	23	♏	1
6	34	51	8	14	13	6	9	1	2
6	39	11	9	15	14	6	55	2	3
6	43	31	10	16	15	7	40	2	4
6	47	51	11	16	16	8	26	3	4
6	52	11	12	17	16	9	12	4	5
6	56	31	13	18	17	9	58	5	6
7	0	50	14	19	18	10	43	6	7
7	5	8	15	20	19	11	28	7	8
7	9	26	16	21	20	12	14	8	9
7	13	44	17	22	21	12	59	8	10
7	18	1	18	23	22	13	45	9	11
7	22	18	19	24	23	14	30	10	12
7	26	34	20	25	24	15	15	11	13
7	30	50	21	26	25	16	0	12	14
7	35	5	22	27	25	16	45	13	15
7	39	20	23	28	26	17	30	13	16
7	43	34	24	29	27	18	15	14	17
7	47	47	25	♍	28	18	59	15	18
7	52	0	26	1	29	19	43	16	19
7	56	12	27	2	29	20	27	17	20
8	0	24	28	3	♎	21	11	18	20
8	4	35	29	4	1	21	56	18	21
8	8	45	30	5	2	22	40	19	22

Sidereal Time.			10 ♌	11 ♍	12 ♎	Ascen ♎		2 ♏	3 ♐
H.	M.	S.	°	°	°	°	′	°	°
8	8	45	0	5	2	22	40	19	22
8	12	54	1	5	3	23	24	20	23
8	17	3	2	6	3	24	7	21	24
8	21	11	3	7	4	24	50	22	25
8	25	19	4	8	5	25	34	23	26
8	29	26	5	9	6	26	18	23	27
8	33	31	6	10	7	27	1	24	28
8	37	37	7	11	8	27	44	25	29
8	41	41	8	12	8	28	26	26	♑
8	45	45	9	13	9	29	8	27	1
8	49	48	10	14	10	29	50	27	2
8	53	51	11	15	11	0 ♏	32	28	3
8	57	52	12	16	12	1	15	29	4
9	1	53	13	17	12	1	58	♐	4
9	5	53	14	18	13	2	39	1	5
9	9	53	15	18	14	3	21	1	6
9	13	52	16	19	15	4	3	2	7
9	17	50	17	20	16	4	44	3	8
9	21	47	18	21	16	5	26	3	9
9	25	44	19	22	17	6	7	4	10
9	29	40	20	23	18	6	48	5	11
9	33	35	21	24	18	7	29	5	12
9	37	29	22	25	19	8	9	6	13
9	41	23	23	26	20	8	50	7	14
9	45	16	24	27	21	9	31	8	15
9	49	9	25	28	22	10	11	9	16
9	53	1	26	28	23	10	51	9	17
9	56	52	27	29	23	11	32	10	18
10	0	43	28	♎	24	12	12	11	19
10	4	3[illegible]	29	1	25	12	53	12	20
10	8	2[illegible]	30	2	26	13	33	13	20

Sidereal Time.			10 ♍	11 ♎	12 ♎	Ascen ♏		2 ♐	3 ♑
H.	M.	S.	°	°	°	°	′	°	°
10	8	23	0	2	26	13	33	13	20
10	12	12	1	3	26	14	13	14	21
10	16	0	2	4	27	14	53	15	22
10	19	48	3	5	28	15	33	15	23
10	23	35	4	5	29	16	13	16	24
10	27	22	5	6	29	16	52	17	25
10	31	8	6	7	♏	17	32	18	26
10	34	54	7	8	1	18	12	19	27
10	38	40	8	9	2	18	52	20	28
10	42	25	9	10	2	19	31	20	29
10	46	9	10	11	3	20	11	21	♒
10	49	53	11	11	4	20	50	22	1
10	53	37	12	12	4	21	30	23	2
10	57	20	13	13	5	22	9	24	3
11	1	3	14	14	6	22	49	24	4
11	4	46	15	15	7	23	28	25	5
11	8	28	16	16	7	24	8	26	6
11	12	10	17	17	8	24	47	27	8
11	15	52	18	17	9	25	27	28	9
11	19	34	19	18	10	26	6	29	10
11	23	15	20	19	10	26	45	♑	11
11	26	56	21	20	11	27	25	0	12
11	30	37	22	21	12	28	5	1	13
11	34	18	23	22	13	28	44	2	14
11	37	58	24	23	13	29	24	3	15
11	41	39	25	23	14	0 ♐	3	4	16
11	45	19	26	24	15	0	43	5	17
11	49	0	27	25	15	1	23	6	18
11	52	40	28	26	16	2	3	6	19
11	56	20	29	27	17	2	43	7	20
12	0	0	30	27	17	3	23	8	21

TABLES OF HOUSES FOR LONDON, *Latitude* 51° 32′ *N.*

Sidereal Time.			10 ♎	11 ♎	12 ♏	Ascen ♐		2 ♑	3 ♒
H.	M.	S.	°	°	°	°	′	°	°
12	0	0	0	27	17	3	23	8	21
12	3	40	1	28	18	4	4	9	23
12	7	20	2	29	19	4	45	10	24
12	11	0	3	♏	20	5	26	11	25
12	14	41	4	1	20	6	7	12	26
12	18	21	5	1	21	6	48	13	27
12	22	2	6	2	22	7	29	14	28
12	25	42	7	3	23	8	10	15	29
12	29	23	8	4	23	8	51	16	♓
12	33	4	9	5	24	9	33	17	2
12	36	45	10	6	25	10	15	18	3
12	40	26	11	6	25	10	57	19	4
12	44	8	12	7	26	11	40	20	5
12	47	50	13	8	27	12	22	21	6
12	51	32	14	9	28	13	4	22	7
12	55	14	15	10	28	13	47	23	9
12	58	57	16	11	29	14	30	24	10
13	2	40	17	11	♐	15	14	25	11
13	6	23	18	12	1	15	59	26	12
13	10	7	19	13	1	16	44	27	13
13	13	51	20	14	2	17	29	28	15
13	17	35	21	15	3	18	14	29	16
13	21	20	22	16	4	19	0	♒	17
13	25	6	23	16	4	19	45	1	18
13	28	52	24	17	5	20	31	2	20
13	32	38	25	18	6	21	18	4	21
13	36	25	26	19	7	22	6	5	22
13	40	12	27	20	7	22	54	6	23
13	44	0	28	21	8	23	42	7	25
13	47	48	29	21	9	24	31	8	26
13	51	37	30	22	10	25	20	10	27

Sidereal Time.			10 ♏	11 ♏	12 ♐	Ascen ♐		2 ♒	3 ♓
H.	M.	S.	°	°	°	°	′	°	°
13	51	37	0	22	10	25	20	10	27
13	55	27	1	23	11	26	10	11	28
13	59	17	2	24	11	27	2	12	♈
14	3	8	3	25	12	27	53	14	1
14	6	59	4	26	13	28	45	15	2
14	10	51	5	26	14	29	36	16	4
14	14	44	6	27	15	0 ♑	29	18	5
14	18	37	7	28	15	1	23	19	6
14	22	31	8	29	16	2	18	20	8
14	26	25	9	♐	17	3	14	22	9
14	30	20	10	1	18	4	11	23	10
14	34	16	11	2	19	5	9	25	11
14	38	13	12	2	20	6	7	26	13
14	42	10	13	3	20	7	6	28	14
14	46	8	14	4	21	8	6	29	15
14	50	7	15	5	22	9	8	♓	17
14	54	7	16	6	23	10	11	2	18
14	58	7	17	7	24	11	15	4	19
15	2	8	18	8	25	12	20	6	21
15	6	9	19	9	26	13	27	8	22
15	10	12	20	9	27	14	35	9	23
15	14	15	21	10	27	15	43	11	24
15	18	19	22	11	28	16	52	13	26
15	22	23	23	12	29	18	3	14	27
15	26	29	24	13	♑	19	16	16	28
15	30	35	25	14	1	20	32	17	29
15	34	41	26	15	2	21	48	19	♉
15	38	49	27	16	3	23	8	21	2
15	42	57	28	17	4	24	29	22	3
15	47	6	29	18	5	25	51	24	5
15	51	15	30	18	6	27	15	26	6

Sidereal Time.			10 ♐	11 ♐	12 ♑	Ascen ♑		2 ♓	3 ♉
H.	M.	S.	°	°	°	°	′	°	°
15	51	15	0	18	6	27	15	26	6
15	55	25	1	19	7	28	42	28	7
15	59	36	2	20	8	0 ♒	11	♈	9
16	3	48	3	21	9	1	42	2	10
16	8	0	4	22	10	3	16	3	11
16	12	13	5	23	11	4	53	5	12
16	16	26	6	24	12	6	32	7	14
16	20	40	7	25	13	8	13	9	15
16	24	55	8	26	14	9	57	11	16
16	29	10	9	27	16	11	44	12	17
16	33	26	10	28	17	13	34	14	18
16	37	42	11	29	18	15	26	16	20
16	41	59	12	♑	19	17	20	18	21
16	46	16	13	1	20	19	18	20	22
16	50	34	14	2	21	21	22	21	23
16	54	52	15	3	22	23	29	23	25
16	59	10	16	4	24	25	36	25	26
17	3	29	17	5	25	27	46	27	27
17	7	49	18	6	26	0 ♓	0	28	28
17	12	9	19	7	27	2	19	♉	29
17	16	29	20	8	29	4	40	2	♊
17	20	49	21	9	♒	7	2	3	1
17	25	9	22	10	1	9	26	5	2
17	29	30	23	11	3	11	54	7	3
17	33	51	24	12	4	14	24	8	5
17	38	12	25	13	5	17	0	10	6
17	42	34	26	14	7	19	33	11	7
17	46	55	27	15	8	22	6	13	8
17	51	17	28	16	10	24	40	14	9
17	55	38	29	17	11	27	20	16	10
18	0	0	30	18	13	30	0	17	11

Sidereal Time.			10 ♑	11 ♑	12 ♒	Ascen ♈		2 ♉	3 ♊
H.	M.	S.	°	°	°	°	′	°	°
18	0	0	0	18	13	0	0	17	11
18	4	22	1	20	14	2	39	19	13
18	8	43	2	21	16	5	19	20	14
18	13	5	3	22	17	7	55	22	15
18	17	26	4	23	19	10	29	23	16
18	21	48	5	24	20	13	2	25	17
18	26	9	6	25	22	15	36	26	18
18	30	30	7	26	23	18	6	28	19
18	34	51	8	27	25	20	34	29	20
18	39	11	9	29	27	22	59	♊	21
18	43	31	10	♒	28	25	22	1	22
18	47	51	11	1	♓	27	42	2	23
18	52	11	12	2	2	29	58	4	24
18	56	31	13	3	3	2 ♉	13	5	25
19	0	50	14	4	5	4	24	6	26
19	5	8	15	6	7	6	30	8	27
19	9	26	16	7	9	8	36	9	28
19	13	44	17	8	10	10	40	10	29
19	18	1	18	9	12	12	39	11	♋
19	22	18	19	10	14	14	35	12	1
19	26	34	20	12	16	16	28	13	2
19	30	50	21	13	18	18	17	14	3
19	35	5	22	14	19	20	3	16	4
19	39	20	23	15	21	21	48	17	5
19	43	34	24	16	23	23	29	18	6
19	47	47	25	18	25	25	9	19	7
19	52	0	26	19	27	26	45	20	8
19	56	12	27	20	28	28	18	21	9
20	0	24	28	21	♈	29	49	22	10
20	4	35	29	23	2	1 ♊	19	23	11
20	8	45	30	24	4	2	45	24	12

Sidereal Time.			10 ♒	11 ♒	12 ♈	Ascen ♊		2 ♊	3 ♋
H.	M.	S.	°	°	°	°	′	°	°
20	8	45	0	24	4	2	45	24	12
20	12	54	1	25	6	4	9	25	12
20	17	3	2	27	7	5	32	26	13
20	21	11	3	28	9	6	53	27	14
20	25	19	4	29	11	8	12	28	15
20	29	26	5	♓	13	9	27	29	16
20	33	31	6	2	14	10	43	♋	17
20	37	37	7	3	16	11	58	1	18
20	41	41	8	4	18	13	9	2	19
20	45	45	9	6	19	14	18	3	20
20	49	48	10	7	21	15	25	3	21
20	53	51	11	8	23	16	32	4	21
20	57	52	12	9	24	17	39	5	22
21	1	53	13	11	26	18	44	6	23
21	5	53	14	12	28	19	48	7	24
21	9	53	15	13	29	20	51	8	25
21	13	52	16	15	♉	21	53	9	26
21	17	50	17	16	2	22	53	10	27
21	21	47	18	17	4	23	52	10	28
21	25	44	19	19	5	24	51	11	28
21	29	40	20	20	7	25	48	12	29
21	33	35	21	22	8	26	44	13	♌
21	37	29	22	23	10	27	40	14	1
21	41	23	23	24	11	28	34	15	2
21	45	16	24	25	13	29	29	15	3
21	49	9	25	26	14	0 ♋	22	16	4
21	53	1	26	28	15	1	15	17	4
21	56	52	27	29	16	2	7	18	5
22	0	43	28	♈	18	2	57	19	6
22	4	33	29	2	19	3	48	19	7
22	8	23	30	3	20	4	38	20	8

Sidereal Time.			10 ♓	11 ♈	12 ♉	Ascen ♋		2 ♋	3 ♌
H.	M.	S.	°	°	°	°	′	°	°
22	8	23	0	3	20	4	38	20	8
22	12	12	1	4	21	5	28	21	8
22	16	0	2	6	23	6	17	22	9
22	19	48	3	7	24	7	5	23	10
22	23	35	4	8	25	7	53	23	11
22	27	22	5	9	26	8	42	24	12
22	31	8	6	10	28	9	29	25	13
22	34	54	7	12	29	10	16	26	14
22	38	40	8	13	♊	11	2	26	14
22	42	25	9	14	1	11	47	27	15
22	46	9	10	15	2	12	31	28	16
22	49	53	11	17	3	13	16	29	17
22	53	37	12	18	4	14	1	29	18
22	57	20	13	19	5	14	45	♌	19
23	1	3	14	20	6	15	28	1	19
23	4	46	15	21	7	16	11	2	20
23	8	28	16	23	8	16	54	2	21
23	12	10	17	24	9	17	37	3	22
23	15	52	18	25	10	18	20	4	23
23	19	34	19	26	11	19	3	5	24
23	23	15	20	27	12	19	45	5	24
23	26	56	21	29	13	20	26	6	25
23	30	37	22	♉	14	21	8	7	26
23	34	18	23	1	15	21	50	7	27
23	37	58	24	2	16	22	31	8	28
23	41	39	25	3	17	23	12	9	28
23	45	19	26	4	18	23	53	9	29
23	49	0	27	5	19	24	32	10	♍
23	52	40	28	6	20	25	15	11	1
23	56	20	29	8	21	25	56	12	2
24	0	0	30	9	22	26	36	13	3

TABLES OF HOUSES FOR LIVERPOOL, Latitude 53° 25′ N.

Sidereal Time.			10 ♈	11 ♉	12 ♊	Ascen ♋		2 ♌	3 ♍
H.	M.	S.	°	°	°	°	′	°	°
0	0	0	0	9	24	28	12	14	3
0	3	40	1	10	25	28	51	14	4
0	7	20	2	12	25	29	30	15	4
0	11	0	3	13	26	0 ♌	9	16	5
0	14	41	4	14	27	0	48	17	6
0	18	21	5	15	28	1	27	17	7
0	22	2	6	16	29	2	6	18	8
0	25	42	7	17	♋	2	44	19	9
0	29	23	8	18	1	3	22	19	10
0	33	4	9	19	1	4	1	20	10
0	36	45	10	20	2	4	39	21	11
0	40	26	11	21	3	5	18	22	12
0	44	8	12	22	4	5	56	22	13
0	47	50	13	23	5	6	34	23	14
0	51	32	14	24	6	7	13	24	14
0	55	14	15	25	6	7	51	24	15
0	58	57	16	26	7	8	30	25	16
1	2	40	17	27	8	9	8	26	17
1	6	23	18	28	9	9	47	26	18
1	10	7	19	29	10	10	25	27	19
1	13	51	20	♊	11	11	4	28	19
1	17	35	21	1	11	11	43	28	20
1	21	20	22	2	12	12	21	29	21
1	25	6	23	3	13	13	0	♍	22
1	28	52	24	4	14	13	39	1	23
1	32	38	25	5	15	14	17	1	24
1	36	25	26	6	15	14	56	2	25
1	40	12	27	7	16	15	35	3	25
1	44	0	28	8	17	16	14	3	26
1	47	48	29	9	18	16	53	4	27
1	51	37	30	10	18	17	32	5	28

Sidereal Time.			10 ♉	11 ♊	12 ♋	Ascen ♌		2 ♍	3 ♍
H.	M.	S.	°	°	°	°	′	°	°
1	51	37	0	10	18	17	32	5	28
1	55	27	1	11	19	18	11	6	29
1	59	17	2	12	20	18	51	6	♎
2	3	8	3	13	21	19	30	7	1
2	6	59	4	14	22	20	9	8	2
2	10	51	5	15	22	20	49	9	2
2	14	44	6	16	23	21	28	9	3
2	18	37	7	17	24	22	8	10	4
2	22	31	8	18	25	22	48	11	5
2	26	25	9	19	25	23	28	12	6
2	30	20	10	20	26	24	8	12	7
2	34	16	11	21	27	24	48	13	8
2	38	13	12	22	28	25	28	14	9
2	42	10	13	23	29	26	8	15	10
2	46	8	14	24	29	26	49	15	10
2	50	7	15	25	♌	27	29	16	11
2	54	7	16	26	1	28	10	17	12
2	58	7	17	27	2	28	51	18	13
3	2	8	18	28	2	29	32	19	14
3	6	9	19	29	3	0 ♍	13	19	15
3	10	12	20	29	4	0	54	20	16
3	14	15	21	♋	5	1	36	21	17
3	18	19	22	1	5	2	17	22	18
3	22	23	23	2	6	2	59	23	19
3	26	29	24	3	7	3	41	23	20
3	30	35	25	4	8	4	23	24	21
3	34	41	26	5	9	5	5	25	22
3	38	49	27	6	10	5	47	26	22
3	42	57	28	7	10	6	29	27	23
3	47	6	29	8	11	7	12	27	24
3	51	15	30	9	12	7	55	28	25

Sidereal Time.			10 ♊	11 ♋	12 ♌	Ascen ♍		2 ♍	3 ♎
H.	M.	S.	°	°	°	°	′	°	°
3	51	15	0	9	12	7	55	28	25
3	55	25	1	10	13	8	37	29	26
3	59	36	2	11	13	9	20	♎	27
4	3	48	3	12	14	10	3	1	28
4	8	0	4	12	15	10	46	2	29
4	12	13	5	13	16	11	30	2	♏
4	16	26	6	14	17	12	13	3	1
4	20	40	7	15	18	12	56	4	2
4	24	55	8	16	18	13	40	5	3
4	29	10	9	17	19	14	24	6	4
4	33	26	10	18	20	15	8	7	5
4	37	42	11	19	21	15	52	7	6
4	41	59	12	20	21	16	36	8	6
4	46	16	13	21	22	17	20	9	7
4	50	34	14	22	23	18	4	10	8
4	54	52	15	23	24	18	48	11	9
4	59	10	16	24	25	19	32	12	10
5	3	29	17	24	26	20	17	12	11
5	7	49	18	25	26	21	1	13	12
5	12	9	19	26	27	21	46	14	13
5	16	29	20	27	28	22	31	15	14
5	20	49	21	28	29	23	16	16	15
5	25	9	22	29	♍	24	0	17	16
5	29	30	23	♌	1	24	45	18	17
5	33	51	24	1	1	25	30	18	18
5	38	12	25	2	2	26	15	19	19
5	42	34	26	3	3	27	0	20	20
5	46	55	27	4	4	27	45	21	21
5	51	17	28	5	5	28	30	22	21
5	55	38	29	6	6	29	15	23	22
6	0	0	30	7	7	30	0	23	23

Sidereal Time.			10 ♋	11 ♌	12 ♍	Ascen ♎		2 ♎	3 ♏
H.	M.	S.	°	°	°	°	′	°	°
6	0	0	0	7	7	0	0	23	23
6	4	22	1	8	7	0	45	24	24
6	8	43	2	9	8	1	30	25	25
6	13	5	3	9	9	2	15	26	26
6	17	26	4	10	10	3	0	27	27
6	21	48	5	11	11	3	45	28	28
6	26	9	6	12	12	4	30	29	29
6	30	30	7	13	12	5	15	29	♐
6	34	51	8	14	13	6	0	♏	1
6	39	11	9	15	14	6	44	1	2
6	43	31	10	16	15	7	29	2	3
6	47	51	11	17	16	8	14	3	4
6	52	11	12	18	17	8	59	4	5
6	56	31	13	19	18	9	43	4	6
7	0	50	14	20	18	10	27	5	6
7	5	8	15	21	19	11	11	6	7
7	9	26	16	22	20	11	56	7	8
7	13	44	17	23	21	12	40	8	9
7	18	1	18	24	22	13	24	8	10
7	22	18	19	24	23	14	8	9	11
7	26	34	20	25	23	14	52	10	12
7	30	50	21	26	24	15	36	11	13
7	35	5	22	27	25	16	20	12	14
7	39	20	23	28	26	17	4	13	15
7	43	34	24	29	27	17	47	13	16
7	47	47	25	♍	28	18	30	14	17
7	52	0	26	1	28	19	13	15	18
7	56	12	27	2	29	19	57	16	18
8	0	24	28	3	♎	20	40	17	19
8	4	35	29	4	1	21	23	17	20
8	8	45	30	5	2	22	5	18	21

Sidereal Time.			10 ♌	11 ♍	12 ♎	Ascen ♎		2 ♏	3 ♐
H.	M.	S.	°	°	°	°	′	°	°
8	8	45	0	5	2	22	5	18	21
8	12	54	1	6	2	22	48	19	22
8	17	3	2	7	3	23	30	20	23
8	21	11	3	8	4	24	13	20	24
8	25	19	4	8	5	24	55	21	25
8	29	26	5	9	6	25	37	22	26
8	33	31	6	10	7	26	19	23	27
8	37	37	7	11	7	27	1	24	28
8	41	41	8	12	8	27	43	25	29
8	45	45	9	13	9	28	24	25	♑
8	49	48	10	14	10	29	6	26	1
8	53	51	11	15	11	29	47	27	1
8	57	52	12	16	11	0 ♏	28	28	2
9	1	53	13	17	12	1	9	28	3
9	5	53	14	18	13	1	50	29	4
9	9	53	15	19	14	2	31	♐	5
9	13	52	16	19	15	3	11	1	6
9	17	50	17	20	15	3	52	1	7
9	21	47	18	21	16	4	32	2	8
9	25	44	19	22	17	5	12	3	9
9	29	40	20	23	18	5	52	4	10
9	33	35	21	24	18	6	32	5	11
9	37	29	22	25	19	7	12	5	12
9	41	23	23	26	20	7	52	6	13
9	45	16	24	27	21	8	32	7	14
9	49	9	25	27	21	9	12	8	15
9	53	1	26	28	22	9	51	8	16
9	56	52	27	29	23	10	30	9	17
10	0	43	28	♎	24	11	9	10	17
10	4	33	29	1	24	11	49	11	18
10	8	23	30	2	25	12	28	11	19

Sidereal Time.			10 ♍	11 ♎	12 ♎	Ascen ♏		2 ♐	3 ♑
H.	M.	S.	°	°	°	°	′	°	°
10	8	23	0	2	25	12	28	11	19
10	12	12	1	3	26	13	6	12	20
10	16	0	2	4	27	13	45	13	21
10	19	48	3	4	27	14	25	14	22
10	23	35	4	5	28	15	4	15	23
10	27	22	5	6	29	15	42	15	24
10	31	8	6	7	29	16	21	16	25
10	34	54	7	8	♏	17	0	17	26
10	38	40	8	9	1	17	39	18	27
10	42	25	9	10	2	18	17	18	28
10	46	9	10	10	2	18	55	19	29
10	49	53	11	11	3	19	34	20	♒
10	53	37	12	12	4	20	13	21	1
10	57	20	13	13	4	20	52	22	2
11	1	3	14	14	5	21	30	22	3
11	4	46	15	15	6	22	8	23	5
11	8	28	16	16	7	22	46	24	6
11	12	10	17	16	7	23	25	25	7
11	15	52	18	17	8	24	4	26	8
11	19	34	19	18	9	24	42	26	9
11	23	15	20	19	9	25	21	27	10
11	26	56	21	20	10	25	59	28	11
11	30	37	22	20	11	26	38	29	12
11	34	18	23	21	12	27	16	♑	13
11	37	58	24	22	12	27	54	1	14
11	41	39	25	23	13	28	33	1	15
11	45	19	26	24	14	29	11	2	16
11	49	0	27	25	14	29	50	3	17
11	52	40	28	26	15	0 ♐	30	4	18
11	56	20	29	26	16	1	9	5	20
12	0	0	30	27	16	1	48	6	21

TABLES OF HOUSES FOR LIVERPOOL, Latitude 53° 25′ N

Sidereal Time. H.	M.	S.	10 ♎ °	11 ♎ °	12 ♏ °	Ascen ♐ °	′	2 ♑ °	3 ♒ °
12	0	0	0	27	16	1	48	6	21
12	3	40	1	28	17	2	27	7	22
12	7	20	2	29	18	3	6	8	23
12	11	0	3	♏	18	3	46	9	24
12	14	41	4	0	19	4	25	10	25
12	18	21	5	1	20	5	6	10	26
12	22	2	6	2	21	5	46	11	28
12	25	42	7	3	21	6	26	12	29
12	29	23	8	4	22	7	6	13	♓
12	33	4	9	4	23	7	46	14	1
12	36	45	10	5	24	8	27	15	2
12	40	26	11	6	24	9	8	16	3
12	44	8	12	7	25	9	49	17	5
12	47	50	13	8	26	10	30	18	6
12	51	32	14	9	26	11	12	19	7
12	55	14	15	9	27	11	54	20	8
12	58	57	16	10	28	12	36	21	10
13	2	40	17	11	28	13	19	22	11
13	6	23	18	12	29	14	2	23	12
13	10	7	19	13	♐	14	45	25	13
13	13	51	20	13	1	15	28	26	15
13	17	35	21	14	1	16	12	27	16
13	21	20	22	15	2	16	56	28	17
13	25	6	23	16	3	17	41	29	18
13	28	52	24	17	4	18	26	♒	19
13	32	38	25	17	4	19	11	1	21
13	36	25	26	18	5	19	57	3	22
13	40	12	27	19	6	20	44	4	23
13	44	0	28	20	7	21	31	5	24
13	47	48	29	21	7	22	18	7	26
13	51	37	30	21	8	23	6	8	27

Sidereal Time. H.	M.	S.	10 ♏ °	11 ♏ °	12 ♐ °	Ascen ♐ °	′	2 ♒ °	3 ♓ °
13	51	37	0	21	8	23	6	8	27
13	55	27	1	22	9	23	55	9	28
13	59	17	2	23	10	24	43	10	♈
14	3	8	3	24	10	25	33	12	1
14	6	59	4	25	11	26	23	13	2
14	10	51	5	26	12	27	14	15	4
14	14	44	6	26	13	28	6	16	5
14	18	37	7	27	13	28	59	18	6
14	22	31	8	28	14	29	52	19	8
14	26	25	9	29	15	0 ♑	46	20	9
14	30	20	10	♐	16	1	41	22	10
14	34	16	11	1	17	2	36	23	11
14	38	13	12	2	18	3	33	25	13
14	42	10	13	2	18	4	30	26	14
14	46	8	14	3	19	5	29	28	16
14	50	7	15	4	20	6	29	♓	17
14	54	7	16	5	21	7	30	1	18
14	58	7	17	6	22	8	32	3	20
15	2	8	18	7	23	9	35	5	21
15	6	9	19	8	24	10	39	6	22
15	10	12	20	8	24	11	45	8	23
15	14	15	21	9	25	12	52	10	25
15	18	19	22	10	26	14	1	11	26
15	22	23	23	11	27	15	11	13	27
15	26	29	24	12	28	16	23	15	29
15	30	35	25	13	29	17	37	17	♉
15	34	41	26	14	♑	18	53	19	1
15	38	49	27	15	1	20	10	21	3
15	42	57	28	16	2	21	29	22	4
15	47	6	29	16	3	22	51	24	5
15	51	15	30	17	4	24	15	26	7

Sidereal Time. H.	M.	S.	10 ♐ °	11 ♐ °	12 ♑ °	Ascen ♑ °	′	2 ♓ °	3 ♉ °
15	51	15	0	17	4	24	15	26	7
15	55	25	1	18	5	25	41	28	8
15	59	36	2	19	6	27	10	♈	9
16	3	48	3	20	7	28	41	2	10
16	8	0	4	21	8	0 ♒	14	4	12
16	12	13	5	22	9	1	50	5	13
16	16	26	6	23	10	3	30	7	14
16	20	40	7	24	11	5	13	9	15
16	24	55	8	25	12	6	58	11	17
16	29	10	9	26	13	8	46	13	18
16	33	26	10	27	14	10	38	15	19
16	37	42	11	28	15	12	32	17	20
16	41	59	12	29	16	14	31	19	22
16	46	16	13	♑	18	16	33	20	23
16	50	34	14	1	19	18	40	22	24
16	54	52	15	2	20	20	50	24	25
16	59	10	16	3	21	23	4	26	26
17	3	29	17	4	22	25	21	28	28
17	7	49	18	5	24	27	42	29	29
17	12	9	19	6	25	0 ♓	8	♉	♊
17	16	29	20	7	26	2	37	3	1
17	20	49	21	8	28	5	10	5	3
17	25	9	22	9	29	7	46	6	4
17	29	30	23	10	♒	10	24	8	5
17	33	51	24	11	2	13	7	10	6
17	38	12	25	12	3	15	52	11	7
17	42	34	26	13	4	18	38	13	8
17	46	55	27	14	6	21	27	15	9
17	51	17	28	15	7	24	17	16	10
17	55	38	29	16	9	27	8	18	12
18	0	0	30	17	11	30	0	19	13

Sidereal Time. H.	M.	S.	10 ♑ °	11 ♑ °	12 ♒ °	Ascen ♈ °	′	2 ♉ °	3 ♊ °
18	0	0	0	17	11	0	0	19	13
18	4	22	1	18	12	2	52	21	14
18	8	43	2	20	14	5	43	23	15
18	13	5	3	21	15	8	33	24	16
18	17	26	4	22	17	11	22	25	17
18	21	48	5	23	19	14	8	27	18
18	26	9	6	24	20	16	53	28	19
18	30	30	7	25	22	19	36	♊	20
18	34	51	8	26	24	22	14	1	21
18	39	11	9	27	25	24	50	2	22
18	43	31	10	29	27	27	23	4	23
18	47	51	11	♒	28	29	52	5	24
18	52	11	12	1	♓	2 ♉	18	6	25
18	56	31	13	2	2	4	39	8	26
19	0	50	14	4	4	6	56	9	27
19	5	8	15	5	6	9	10	10	28
19	9	26	16	6	8	11	20	11	29
19	13	44	17	7	10	13	27	12	♋
19	18	1	18	8	11	15	29	14	1
19	22	18	19	9	13	17	28	15	2
19	26	34	20	11	15	19	22	16	3
19	30	50	21	12	17	21	14	17	4
19	35	5	22	13	19	23	2	18	5
19	39	20	23	15	21	24	47	19	6
19	43	34	24	16	23	26	30	20	7
19	47	47	25	17	25	28	10	21	8
19	52	0	26	18	26	29	46	22	9
19	56	12	27	20	28	1 ♊	19	23	10
20	0	24	28	21	♈	2	50	24	11
20	4	35	29	22	2	4	19	25	12
20	8	45	30	23	4	5	45	26	13

Sidereal Time. H.	M.	S.	10 ♒ °	11 ♒ °	12 ♈ °	Ascen ♊ °	′	2 ♊ °	3 ♋ °
20	8	45	0	23	4	5	45	26	13
20	12	54	1	25	6	7	9	27	14
20	17	3	2	26	8	8	31	28	14
20	21	11	3	27	9	9	50	29	15
20	25	19	4	29	11	11	7	♋	16
20	29	26	5	♓	13	12	23	1	17
20	33	31	6	1	15	13	37	2	18
20	37	37	7	3	17	14	49	3	19
20	41	41	8	4	19	15	59	4	20
20	45	45	9	5	20	17	8	5	21
20	49	48	10	7	22	18	15	6	22
20	53	51	11	8	24	19	21	7	22
20	57	52	12	10	25	20	25	7	23
21	1	53	13	11	27	21	28	8	24
21	5	53	14	12	29	22	30	9	25
21	9	53	15	13	♉	23	31	10	26
21	13	52	16	14	2	24	31	11	27
21	17	50	17	16	4	25	30	12	28
21	21	47	18	17	5	26	27	12	28
21	25	44	19	18	7	27	24	13	29
21	29	40	20	20	8	28	19	14	♌
21	33	35	21	21	10	29	14	15	1
21	37	29	22	22	11	0 ♋	8	16	2
21	41	23	23	24	12	1	1	17	3
21	45	16	24	25	14	1	54	17	4
21	49	9	25	26	15	2	46	18	4
21	53	1	26	28	17	3	37	19	5
21	56	52	27	29	18	4	27	20	6
22	0	43	28	♈	20	5	17	20	7
22	4	33	29	2	21	6	5	21	8
22	8	23	30	3	22	6	54	22	8

Sidereal Time. H.	M.	S.	10 ♓ °	11 ♈ °	12 ♉ °	Ascen ♋ °	′	2 ♋ °	3 ♌ °
22	8	23	0	3	22	6	54	22	8
22	12	12	1	4	23	7	42	23	9
22	16	0	2	5	25	8	29	23	10
22	19	48	3	7	26	9	16	24	11
22	23	35	4	8	27	10	3	25	12
22	27	22	5	9	29	10	49	26	13
22	31	8	6	11	♊	11	34	26	13
22	34	54	7	12	1	12	19	27	14
22	38	40	8	13	2	13	3	28	15
22	42	25	9	14	3	13	48	29	16
22	46	9	10	16	4	14	32	29	17
22	49	53	11	17	5	15	15	♌	17
22	53	37	12	18	7	15	58	1	18
22	57	20	13	19	8	16	41	2	19
23	1	3	14	20	9	17	24	2	20
23	4	46	15	22	10	18	6	3	21
23	8	28	16	23	11	18	48	4	21
23	12	10	17	24	12	19	30	4	22
23	15	52	18	25	13	20	11	5	23
23	19	34	19	27	14	20	52	6	24
23	23	15	20	28	15	21	33	6	25
23	26	56	21	29	16	22	14	7	26
23	30	37	22	♉	17	22	54	8	26
23	34	18	23	1	18	23	34	9	27
23	37	58	24	2	19	24	14	9	28
23	41	39	25	4	20	24	54	10	29
23	45	19	26	5	21	25	35	11	♍
23	49	0	27	6	22	26	14	11	0
23	52	40	28	7	22	26	54	12	1
23	56	20	29	8	23	27	33	13	2
24	0	0	30	9	24	28	12	14	3

TABLES OF HOUSES FOR NEW YORK, *Latitude* 40° 43′ *N.*

Sidereal Time H.	M.	S.	10 ♈ °	11 ♉ °	12 ♊ °	Ascen ♋ °	′	2 ♌ °	3 ♍ °
0	0	0	0	6	15	18	53	8	1
0	3	40	1	7	16	19	38	9	2
0	7	20	2	8	17	20	23	10	3
0	11	0	3	9	18	21	12	11	4
0	14	41	4	11	19	21	55	12	5
0	18	21	5	12	20	22	40	12	5
0	22	2	6	13	21	23	24	13	6
0	25	42	7	14	22	24	8	14	7
0	29	23	8	15	23	24	54	15	8
0	33	4	9	16	23	25	37	15	9
0	36	45	10	17	24	26	22	16	10
0	40	26	11	18	25	27	5	17	11
0	44	8	12	19	26	27	50	18	12
0	47	50	13	20	27	28	33	19	13
0	51	32	14	21	28	29	18	19	13
0	55	14	15	22	28	0 ♌	3	20	14
0	58	57	16	23	29	0	46	21	15
1	2	40	17	24	♋	1	31	22	16
1	6	23	18	25	1	2	14	22	17
1	10	7	19	26	2	2	58	23	18
1	13	51	20	27	3	3	43	24	19
1	17	35	21	28	3	4	27	25	20
1	21	20	22	29	4	5	12	25	21
1	25	6	23	♊	5	5	56	26	22
1	28	52	24	1	6	6	40	27	22
1	32	38	25	2	7	7	25	28	23
1	36	25	26	2	8	8	9	29	24
1	40	12	27	3	9	8	53	♍	25
1	44	0	28	4	10	9	38	1	26
1	47	48	29	5	10	10	24	1	27
1	51	37	30	6	11	11	8	2	28

Sidereal Time H.	M.	S.	10 ♉ °	11 ♊ °	12 ♋ °	Ascen ♌ °	′	2 ♍ °	3 ♍ °
1	51	37	0	6	11	11	8	2	28
1	55	27	1	7	12	11	53	3	29
1	59	17	2	8	13	12	38	4	♎
2	3	8	3	9	14	13	22	5	1
2	6	59	4	10	15	14	8	5	2
2	10	51	5	11	15	14	53	6	3
2	14	44	6	12	16	15	39	7	4
2	18	37	7	13	17	16	24	8	4
2	22	31	8	14	18	17	10	9	5
2	26	25	9	15	19	17	56	10	6
2	30	20	10	16	20	18	41	10	7
2	34	16	11	17	20	19	27	11	8
2	38	13	12	18	21	20	14	12	9
2	42	10	13	19	22	21	0	13	10
2	46	8	14	19	23	21	47	14	11
2	50	7	15	20	24	22	33	15	12
2	54	7	16	21	25	23	20	16	13
2	58	7	17	22	25	24	7	17	14
3	2	8	18	23	26	24	54	17	15
3	6	9	19	24	27	25	42	18	16
3	10	12	20	25	28	26	29	19	17
3	14	15	21	26	29	27	17	20	18
3	18	19	22	27	♌	28	4	21	19
3	22	23	23	28	1	28	52	22	20
3	26	29	24	29	1	29	40	23	21
3	30	35	25	♋	2	0 ♍	29	24	22
3	34	41	26	1	3	1	17	24	23
3	38	49	27	2	4	2	6	25	24
3	42	57	28	3	5	2	55	26	25
3	47	6	29	4	6	3	43	27	26
3	51	15	30	5	7	4	32	28	27

Sidereal Time H.	M.	S.	10 ♊ °	11 ♋ °	12 ♌ °	Ascen ♍ °	′	2 ♍ °	3 ♎ °
3	51	15	0	5	7	4	32	28	27
3	55	25	1	6	8	5	22	29	28
3	59	36	2	6	8	6	10	♎	29
4	3	48	3	7	9	7	0	1	♏
4	8	0	4	8	10	7	49	2	1
4	12	13	5	9	11	8	40	3	2
4	16	26	6	10	12	9	30	4	3
4	20	40	7	11	13	10	19	4	4
4	24	55	8	12	14	11	10	5	5
4	29	10	9	13	15	12	0	6	6
4	33	26	10	14	16	12	51	7	7
4	37	42	11	15	16	13	41	8	8
4	41	59	12	16	17	14	32	9	9
4	46	16	13	17	18	15	23	10	10
4	50	34	14	18	19	16	14	11	11
4	54	52	15	19	20	17	5	12	12
4	59	10	16	20	21	17	56	13	13
5	3	29	17	21	22	18	47	14	14
5	7	49	18	22	23	19	39	15	15
5	12	9	19	23	24	20	30	16	16
5	16	29	20	24	25	21	22	17	17
5	20	49	21	25	25	22	13	18	18
5	25	9	22	26	26	23	5	18	19
5	29	30	23	27	27	23	57	19	20
5	33	51	24	28	28	24	49	20	21
5	38	12	25	29	29	25	40	21	22
5	42	34	26	♌	♍	26	32	22	22
5	46	55	27	1	1	27	25	23	23
5	51	17	28	2	2	28	16	24	24
5	55	38	29	3	3	29	8	25	25
6	0	0	30	4	4	30	0	26	26

Sidereal Time H.	M.	S.	10 ♋ °	11 ♌ °	12 ♍ °	Ascen ♎ °	′	2 ♎ °	3 ♏ °
6	0	0	0	4	4	0	0	26	26
6	4	22	1	5	5	0	52	27	27
6	8	43	2	6	6	1	44	28	28
6	13	5	3	6	7	2	35	29	29
6	17	26	4	7	8	3	28	♏	♐
6	21	48	5	8	9	4	20	1	1
6	26	9	6	9	10	5	11	2	2
6	30	30	7	10	11	6	3	3	3
6	34	51	8	11	12	6	55	3	4
6	39	11	9	12	13	7	47	4	5
6	43	31	10	13	14	8	38	5	6
6	47	51	11	14	15	9	30	6	7
6	52	11	12	15	15	10	21	7	8
6	56	31	13	16	16	11	13	8	9
7	0	50	14	17	17	12	4	9	10
7	5	8	15	18	18	12	55	10	11
7	9	26	16	19	19	13	46	11	12
7	13	44	17	20	20	14	37	12	13
7	18	1	18	21	21	15	28	13	14
7	22	18	19	22	22	16	19	14	15
7	26	34	20	23	23	17	9	14	16
7	30	50	21	24	23	18	0	15	17
7	35	5	22	25	24	18	50	16	18
7	39	20	23	26	25	19	41	17	19
7	43	34	24	27	26	20	30	18	20
7	47	47	25	28	27	21	20	19	21
7	52	0	26	29	28	22	11	20	22
7	56	12	27	♍	29	23	0	21	23
8	0	24	28	1	♎	23	50	21	24
8	4	35	29	2	1	24	38	22	24
8	8	45	30	3	2	25	28	23	25

Sidereal Time H.	M.	S.	10 ♌ °	11 ♍ °	12 ♎ °	Ascen ♎ °	′	2 ♏ °	3 ♐ °
8	8	45	0	3	2	25	28	23	25
8	12	54	1	4	3	26	17	24	26
8	17	3	2	5	4	27	5	25	27
8	21	11	3	6	5	27	54	26	28
8	25	19	4	7	6	28	43	27	29
8	29	26	5	8	7	29	31	28	♑
8	33	31	6	9	7	0 ♏	20	28	1
8	37	37	7	10	8	1	8	29	2
8	41	41	8	11	9	1	56	♐	3
8	45	45	9	12	10	2	43	1	4
8	49	48	10	13	11	3	31	2	5
8	53	51	11	14	12	4	18	3	6
8	57	52	12	15	12	5	6	4	7
9	1	53	13	16	13	5	53	5	8
9	5	53	14	17	14	6	40	5	9
9	9	53	15	18	15	7	27	6	10
9	13	52	16	19	16	8	13	7	10
9	17	50	17	20	17	9	0	8	11
9	21	47	18	21	18	9	46	9	12
9	25	44	19	22	19	10	33	10	13
9	29	40	20	23	19	11	19	10	14
9	33	35	21	24	20	12	4	11	15
9	37	29	22	24	21	12	50	12	16
9	41	23	23	25	22	13	36	13	17
9	45	16	24	26	23	14	21	14	18
9	49	9	25	27	24	15	7	15	19
9	53	1	26	28	24	15	52	15	20
9	56	52	27	29	25	16	38	16	21
10	0	43	28	♎	26	17	22	17	22
10	4	33	29	1	27	18	7	18	23
10	8	23	30	2	28	18	52	19	24

Sidereal Time H.	M.	S.	10 ♍ °	11 ♎ °	12 ♎ °	Ascen ♏ °	′	2 ♐ °	3 ♑ °
10	8	23	0	2	28	18	52	19	24
10	12	12	1	3	29	19	36	20	25
10	16	0	2	4	29	20	22	20	26
10	19	48	3	5	♏	21	7	21	27
10	23	35	4	6	1	21	51	22	28
10	27	22	5	7	1	22	35	23	28
10	31	8	6	7	2	23	20	24	29
10	34	54	7	8	3	24	4	25	♒
10	38	40	8	9	4	24	48	25	1
10	42	25	9	10	5	25	33	26	2
10	46	9	10	11	6	26	17	27	3
10	49	53	11	12	7	27	2	28	4
10	53	37	12	13	7	27	46	29	5
10	57	20	13	14	8	28	29	♑	6
11	1	3	14	15	9	29	14	1	7
11	4	46	15	16	10	29	57	1	8
11	8	28	16	17	11	0 ♐	42	2	9
11	12	10	17	17	11	1	27	3	10
11	15	52	18	18	12	2	10	4	11
11	19	34	19	19	13	2	55	5	12
11	23	15	20	20	14	3	38	6	13
11	26	56	21	21	14	4	23	7	14
11	30	37	22	22	15	5	6	7	15
11	34	18	23	23	16	5	52	8	16
11	37	58	24	23	17	6	36	9	17
11	41	39	25	24	18	7	20	10	18
11	45	19	26	25	18	8	5	11	19
11	49	0	27	26	19	8	48	12	20
11	52	40	28	27	20	9	37	13	22
11	56	20	29	28	21	10	22	14	23
12	0	0	30	29	21	11	7	15	24

TABLES OF HOUSES FOR NEW YORK, Latitude 40° 43′ *N.*

Sidereal Time. H.	M.	S.	10 ♎ °	11 ♎ °	12 ♏ °	Ascen ♐ °	Ascen ′	2 ♑ °	3 ♒ °
12	0	0	0	29	21	11	7	15	24
12	3	40	1	♏	22	11	52	16	25
12	7	20	2	1	23	12	37	17	26
12	11	0	3	1	24	13	19	17	27
12	14	41	4	2	25	14	7	18	28
12	18	21	5	3	25	14	52	19	29
12	22	2	6	4	26	15	38	20	♓
12	25	42	7	5	27	16	23	21	1
12	29	23	8	6	28	17	11	22	2
12	33	4	9	6	28	17	58	23	3
12	36	45	10	7	29	18	45	24	4
12	40	26	11	8	♐	19	32	25	5
12	44	8	12	9	1	20	20	26	7
12	47	50	13	10	2	21	8	27	8
12	51	32	14	11	2	21	57	28	9
12	55	14	15	12	3	22	43	29	10
12	58	57	16	13	4	23	33	♒	11
13	2	40	17	13	5	24	22	1	12
13	6	23	18	14	6	25	11	2	13
13	10	7	19	15	7	26	1	3	15
13	13	51	20	16	7	26	51	5	16
13	17	35	21	17	8	27	40	6	17
13	21	20	22	18	9	28	32	7	18
13	25	6	23	19	10	29	23	8	19
13	28	52	24	19	10	0 ♑	14	9	20
13	32	38	25	20	11	1	7	10	21
13	36	25	26	21	12	2	0	11	23
13	40	12	27	22	13	2	52	12	24
13	44	0	28	23	13	3	46	13	25
13	47	48	29	24	14	4	41	15	26
13	51	37	30	25	15	5	35	16	27

Sidereal Time. H.	M.	S.	10 ♏ °	11 ♏ °	12 ♐ °	Ascen ♑ °	Ascen ′	2 ♒ °	3 ♓ °
13	51	37	0	25	15	5	35	16	27
13	55	27	1	25	16	6	30	17	29
13	59	17	2	26	17	7	27	18	♈
14	3	8	3	27	18	8	23	20	1
14	6	59	4	28	18	9	20	21	2
14	10	51	5	29	19	10	18	22	3
14	14	44	6	♐	20	11	16	23	5
14	18	37	7	1	21	12	15	24	6
14	22	31	8	2	22	13	15	26	7
14	26	25	9	2	23	14	16	27	8
14	30	20	10	3	24	15	17	28	9
14	34	16	11	4	24	16	19	♓	11
14	38	13	12	5	25	17	23	1	12
14	42	10	13	6	26	18	27	2	13
14	46	8	14	7	27	19	32	4	14
14	50	7	15	8	28	20	37	5	16
14	54	7	16	9	29	21	44	6	17
14	58	7	17	10	♑	22	51	8	18
15	2	8	18	10	1	23	59	9	19
15	6	9	19	11	2	25	9	11	20
15	10	12	20	12	3	26	19	12	22
15	14	15	21	13	4	27	31	14	23
15	18	19	22	14	5	28	43	15	24
15	22	23	23	15	6	29	57	16	25
15	26	29	24	16	6	1 ♒	14	18	26
15	30	35	25	17	7	2	28	19	28
15	34	41	26	18	8	3	46	21	29
15	38	49	27	19	9	5	5	22	♉
15	42	57	28	20	10	6	25	24	1
15	47	6	29	21	11	7	46	25	3
15	51	15	30	21	13	9	8	27	4

Sidereal Time. H.	M.	S.	10 ♐ °	11 ♐ °	12 ♑ °	Ascen ♒ °	Ascen ′	2 ♓ °	3 ♉ °
15	51	15	0	21	13	9	8	27	4
15	55	25	1	22	14	10	31	28	5
15	59	36	2	23	15	11	56	♈	6
16	3	48	3	24	16	13	23	1	7
16	8	0	4	25	17	14	50	3	9
16	12	13	5	26	18	16	9	4	10
16	16	26	6	27	19	17	50	6	11
16	20	40	7	28	20	19	22	7	12
16	24	55	8	29	21	20	56	9	13
16	29	10	9	♑	22	22	30	11	15
16	33	26	10	1	23	24	7	12	16
16	37	42	11	2	24	25	44	14	17
16	41	59	12	3	26	27	23	15	18
16	46	16	13	4	27	29	4	17	19
16	50	34	14	5	28	0 ♓	45	18	20
16	54	52	15	6	29	2	27	20	22
16	59	10	16	7	♒	4	11	21	23
17	3	29	17	8	2	5	56	23	24
17	7	49	18	9	3	7	43	24	25
17	12	9	19	10	4	9	30	26	26
17	16	29	20	11	5	11	18	27	27
17	20	49	21	12	7	13	8	29	28
17	25	9	22	13	8	14	57	♉	♊
17	29	30	23	14	9	16	48	2	1
17	33	51	24	15	10	18	41	3	2
17	38	12	25	16	12	20	33	5	3
17	42	34	26	17	13	22	25	6	4
17	46	55	27	19	14	24	19	7	5
17	51	17	28	20	16	26	12	9	6
17	55	38	29	21	17	28	7	10	7
18	0	0	30	22	18	30	0	12	9

Sidereal Time. H.	M.	S.	10 ♑ °	11 ♑ °	12 ♒ °	Ascen ♈ °	Ascen ′	2 ♉ °	3 ♊ °
18	0	0	0	22	18	0	0	12	9
18	4	22	1	23	20	1	53	13	10
18	8	43	2	24	21	3	48	14	11
18	13	5	3	25	23	5	41	16	12
18	17	26	4	26	24	7	35	17	13
18	21	48	5	27	25	9	27	18	14
18	26	9	6	28	27	11	19	20	15
18	30	30	7	29	28	13	12	21	16
18	34	51	8	♒	♓	15	3	22	17
18	39	11	9	2	1	16	52	23	18
18	43	31	10	3	3	18	42	25	19
18	47	51	11	4	4	20	30	26	20
18	52	11	12	5	5	22	17	27	21
18	56	31	13	6	7	24	4	29	22
19	0	50	14	7	9	25	49	♊	23
19	5	8	15	9	10	27	33	1	24
19	9	26	16	10	12	29	15	2	25
19	13	44	17	11	13	0 ♉	56	3	26
19	18	1	18	12	15	2	37	4	27
19	22	18	19	13	16	4	16	6	28
19	26	34	20	14	18	5	53	7	29
19	30	50	21	16	19	7	30	8	♋
19	35	5	22	17	21	9	4	9	1
19	39	20	23	18	22	10	38	10	2
19	43	34	24	19	24	12	10	11	3
19	47	47	25	20	25	13	41	12	4
19	52	0	26	21	27	15	10	13	5
19	56	12	27	23	29	16	37	14	6
20	0	24	28	24	♈	18	4	15	7
20	4	35	29	25	2	19	29	16	8
20	8	45	30	26	3	20	52	17	9

Sidereal Time. H.	M.	S.	10 ♒ °	11 ♒ °	12 ♈ °	Ascen ♉ °	Ascen ′	2 ♊ °	3 ♋ °
20	8	45	0	26	3	20	52	17	9
20	12	54	1	27	5	22	14	18	9
20	17	3	2	29	6	23	35	19	10
20	21	11	3	♓	8	24	55	20	11
20	25	19	4	1	9	26	14	21	12
20	29	26	5	2	11	27	32	22	13
20	33	31	6	3	12	28	46	23	14
20	37	37	7	5	14	0 ♊	3	24	15
20	41	41	8	6	15	1	17	25	16
20	45	45	9	7	16	2	29	26	17
20	49	48	10	8	18	3	41	27	18
20	53	51	11	10	19	4	51	28	19
20	57	52	12	11	21	6	1	29	20
21	1	53	13	12	22	7	9	♋	20
21	5	53	14	13	24	8	16	1	21
21	9	53	15	14	25	9	23	2	22
21	13	52	16	16	26	10	30	3	23
21	17	50	17	17	28	11	33	4	24
21	21	47	18	18	29	12	37	5	25
21	25	44	19	19	♉	13	41	6	26
21	29	40	20	21	2	14	43	6	27
21	33	35	21	22	3	15	44	7	28
21	37	29	22	23	4	16	45	8	28
21	41	23	23	24	6	17	45	9	29
21	45	16	24	25	7	18	44	10	♌
21	49	9	25	27	8	19	42	11	1
21	53	1	26	28	9	20	40	12	2
21	56	52	27	29	11	21	37	12	3
22	0	43	28	♈	12	22	33	13	4
22	4	33	29	1	13	23	30	14	5
22	8	23	30	3	14	24	25	15	5

Sidereal Time. H.	M.	S.	10 ♓ °	11 ♈ °	12 ♉ °	Ascen ♊ °	Ascen ′	2 ♋ °	3 ♌ °
22	8	23	0	3	14	24	25	15	5
22	12	12	1	4	15	25	19	16	6
22	16	0	2	5	17	26	14	17	7
22	19	48	3	6	18	27	8	17	8
22	23	35	4	7	19	28	0	18	9
22	27	22	5	8	20	28	53	19	10
22	31	8	6	10	21	29	46	20	11
22	34	54	7	11	22	0 ♋	37	21	11
22	38	40	8	12	23	1	28	21	12
22	42	25	9	13	24	2	20	22	13
22	46	9	10	14	25	3	9	23	14
22	49	53	11	15	27	3	59	24	15
22	53	37	12	17	28	4	49	24	16
22	57	20	13	18	29	5	38	25	17
23	1	3	14	19	♊	6	27	26	17
23	4	46	15	20	1	7	17	27	18
23	8	28	16	21	2	8	3	28	19
23	12	10	17	22	3	8	52	28	20
23	15	52	18	23	4	9	40	29	21
23	19	34	19	24	5	10	28	♌	22
23	23	15	20	26	6	11	15	1	23
23	26	56	21	27	7	12	2	2	23
23	30	37	22	28	8	12	49	2	24
23	34	18	23	29	9	13	37	3	25
23	37	58	24	♉	10	14	22	4	26
23	41	39	25	1	11	15	8	5	27
23	45	19	26	2	12	15	53	5	28
23	49	0	27	3	12	16	41	6	29
23	52	40	28	4	13	17	23	7	29
23	56	20	29	5	14	18	8	8	♍
24	0	0	30	6	15	18	53	9	1

PROPORTIONAL LOGARITHMS FOR FINDING THE PLANETS' PLACES

DEGREES OR HOURS

Min.	0	1	2	3	4	5	6	7	8	9	10	11	12	13	14	15	Min.
0	3.1584	1.3802	1.0792	9031	7781	6812	6021	5351	4771	4260	3802	3388	3010	2663	2341	2041	0
1	3.1584	1.3730	1.0756	9007	7763	6798	6009	5341	4762	4252	3795	3382	3004	2657	2336	2036	1
2	2.8573	1.3660	1.0720	8983	7745	6784	5997	5330	4753	4244	3788	3375	2998	2652	2330	2032	2
3	2.6812	1.3590	1.0685	8959	7728	6769	5985	5320	4744	4236	3780	3368	2992	2646	2325	2027	3
4	2.5563	1.3522	1.0649	8935	7710	6755	5973	5310	4735	4228	3773	3362	2986	2640	2320	2022	4
5	2.4594	1.3454	1.0614	8912	7692	6741	5961	5300	4726	4220	3766	3355	2980	2635	2315	2017	5
6	2.3802	1.3388	1.0580	8888	7674	6726	5949	5289	4717	4212	3759	3349	2974	2629	2310	2012	6
7	2.3133	1.3323	1.0546	8865	7657	6712	5937	5279	4708	4204	3752	3342	2968	2624	2305	2008	7
8	2.2553	1.3258	1.0511	8842	7639	6698	5925	5269	4699	4196	3745	3336	2962	2618	2300	2003	8
9	2.2041	1.3195	1.0478	8819	7622	6684	5913	5259	4690	4188	3737	3329	2956	2613	2295	1998	9
10	2.1584	1.3133	1.0444	8796	7604	6670	5902	5249	4682	4180	3730	3323	2950	2607	2289	1993	10
11	2.1170	1.3071	1.0411	8773	7587	6656	5890	5239	4673	4172	3723	3316	2944	2602	2284	1988	11
12	2.0792	1.3010	1.0378	8751	7570	6642	5878	5229	4664	4164	3716	3310	2938	2596	2279	1984	12
13	2.0444	1.2950	1.0345	8728	7552	6628	5866	5219	4655	4156	3709	3303	2933	2591	2274	1979	13
14	2.0122	1.2891	1.0313	8706	7535	6614	5855	5209	4646	4148	3702	3297	2927	2585	2269	1974	14
15	1.9823	1.2833	1.0280	8683	7518	6600	5843	5199	4638	4141	3695	3291	2921	2580	2264	1969	15
16	1.9542	1.2775	1.0248	8661	7501	6587	5832	5189	4629	4133	3688	3284	2915	2574	2259	1965	16
17	1.9279	1.2719	1.0216	8639	7484	6573	5820	5179	4620	4125	3681	3278	2909	2569	2254	1960	17
18	1.9031	1.2663	1.0185	8617	7467	6559	5809	5169	4611	4117	3674	3271	2903	2564	2249	1955	18
19	1.8796	1.2607	1.0153	8595	7451	6546	5797	5159	4603	4109	3667	3265	2897	2558	2244	1950	19
20	1.8573	1.2553	1.0122	8573	7434	6532	5786	5149	4594	4102	3660	3258	2891	2553	2239	1946	20
21	1.8361	1.2499	1.0091	8552	7417	6519	5774	5139	4585	4094	3653	3252	2885	2547	2234	1941	21
22	1.8159	1.2445	1.0061	8530	7401	6505	5763	5129	4577	4086	3646	3246	2880	2542	2229	1936	22
23	1.7966	1.2393	1.0030	8509	7384	6492	5752	5120	4568	4079	3639	3239	2874	2536	2223	1932	23
24	1.7781	1.2341	1.0000	8487	7368	6478	5740	5110	4559	4071	3632	3233	2868	2531	2218	1927	24
25	1.7604	1.2289	0.9970	8466	7351	6465	5729	5100	4551	4063	3625	3227	2862	2526	2213	1922	25
26	1.7434	1.2239	0.9940	8445	7335	6451	5718	5090	4542	4055	3618	3220	2856	2520	2208	1917	26
27	1.7270	1.2188	0.9910	8424	7318	6438	5706	5081	4534	4048	3611	3214	2850	2515	2203	1913	27
28	1.7112	1.2139	0.9881	8403	7302	6425	5695	5071	4525	4040	3604	3208	2845	2509	2198	1908	28
29	1.6960	1.2090	0.9852	8382	7286	6412	5684	5061	4516	4032	3597	3201	2839	2504	2193	1903	29
30	1.6812	1.2041	0.9823	8361	7270	6398	5673	5051	4508	4025	3590	3195	2833	2499	2188	1899	30
31	1.6670	1.1993	0.9794	8341	7254	6385	5662	5042	4499	4017	3583	3189	2827	2493	2183	1894	31
32	1.6532	1.1946	0.9765	8320	7238	6372	5651	5032	4491	4010	3576	3183	2821	2488	2178	1889	32
33	1.6398	1.1899	0.9737	8300	7222	6359	5640	5023	4482	4002	3570	3176	2816	2483	2173	1885	33
34	1.6269	1.1852	0.9708	8279	7206	6346	5629	5013	4474	3994	3563	3170	2810	2477	2168	1880	34
35	1.6143	1.1806	0.9680	8259	7190	6333	5618	5003	4466	3987	3556	3164	2804	2472	2164	1875	35
36	1.6021	1.1761	0.9652	8239	7174	6320	5607	4994	4457	3979	3549	3157	2798	2467	2159	1871	36
37	1.5902	1.1716	0.9625	8219	7159	6307	5596	4984	4449	3972	3542	3151	2793	2461	2154	1866	37
38	1.5786	1.1671	0.9597	8199	7143	6294	5585	4975	4440	3964	3535	3145	2787	2456	2149	1862	38
39	1.5673	1.1627	0.9570	8179	7128	6282	5574	4965	4432	3957	3529	3139	2781	2451	2144	1857	39
40	1.5563	1.1584	0.9542	8159	7112	6269	5563	4956	4424	3949	3522	3133	2775	2445	2139	1852	40
41	1.5456	1.1540	0.9515	8140	7097	6256	5552	4947	4415	3942	3515	3126	2770	2440	2134	1848	41
42	1.5351	1.1498	0.9488	8120	7081	6243	5541	4937	4407	3934	3508	3120	2764	2435	2129	1843	42
43	1.5249	1.1455	0.9462	8101	7066	6231	5531	4928	4399	3927	3501	3114	2758	2430	2124	1838	43
44	1.5149	1.1413	0.9435	8081	7050	6218	5520	4918	4390	3919	3495	3108	2753	2424	2119	1834	44
45	1.5051	1.1372	0.9409	8062	7035	6205	5509	4909	4382	3912	3488	3102	2747	2419	2114	1829	45
46	1.4956	1.1331	0.9383	8043	7020	6193	5498	4900	4374	3905	3481	3096	2741	2414	2109	1825	46
47	1.4863	1.1290	0.9356	8023	7005	6180	5488	4890	4365	3897	3475	3089	2736	2409	2104	1820	47
48	1.4771	1.1249	0.9330	8004	6990	6168	5477	4881	4357	3890	3468	3083	2730	2403	2099	1816	48
49	1.4682	1.1209	0.9305	7985	6975	6155	5466	4872	4349	3882	3461	3077	2724	2398	2095	1811	49
50	1.4594	1.1170	0.9279	7966	6960	6143	5456	4863	4341	3875	3454	3071	2719	2393	2090	1806	50
51	1.4508	1.1130	0.9254	7947	6945	6131	5445	4853	4333	3868	3448	3065	2713	2388	2085	1802	51
52	1.4424	1.1091	0.9228	7929	6930	6118	5435	4844	4324	3860	3441	3059	2707	2382	2080	1797	52
53	1.4341	1.1053	0.9203	7910	6915	6106	5424	4835	4316	3853	3434	3053	2702	2377	2075	1793	53
54	1.4260	1.1015	0.9178	7891	6900	6094	5414	4826	4308	3846	3428	3047	2696	2372	2070	1788	54
55	1.4180	1.0977	0.9153	7873	6885	6081	5403	4817	4300	3838	3421	3041	2691	2367	2065	1784	55
56	1.4102	1.0939	0.9128	7854	6871	6069	5393	4808	4292	3831	3415	3034	2685	2362	2061	1779	56
57	1.4025	1.0902	0.9104	7836	6856	6057	5382	4798	4284	3824	3408	3028	2679	2356	2056	1774	57
58	1.3949	1.0865	0.9079	7818	6841	6045	5372	4789	4276	3817	3401	3022	2674	2351	2051	1770	58
59	1.3875	1.0828	0.9055	7800	6827	6033	5361	4780	4268	3809	3395	3016	2668	2346	2046	1765	59
	0	1	2	3	4	5	6	7	8	9	10	11	12	13	14	15	

RULE:—Add proportional log. of planet's daily motion to log. of time from noon, and the sum will be the log. of the motion required. Add this to planet's place at noon, if time be p.m., but subtract if a.m. and the sum will be planet's true place. If Retrograde, subtract for p.m., but add for a.m.

What is the Long. of ☽ August 22, 1997 at 2.15 p.m.?

☽'s daily motion—14° 12′

Prop. Log. of 14° 12′	.2279
Prop. Log. of 2h. 15m.	1.0280
☽'s motion in 2h. 15m. = 1° 20′ or Log.	1.2559

☽'s Long. = 25° ♈ 51′ + 1° 20′ = 27° ♈ 11′

The Daily Motions of the Sun, Moon, Mercury, Venus and Mars will be found on pages 26 to 28.